ELEMENTARY REACTION
KINETICS

ELEMENTARY REACTION KINETICS

J. L. LATHAM, B.Sc., Ph.D., A.R.I.C.

Senior Lecturer in Physical Chemistry
Harris College, Preston

LONDON
BUTTERWORTHS
1964

13,597

ENGLAND:	BUTTERWORTH & CO. (PUBLISHERS) LTD. LONDON: 88 Kingsway, W.C.2
AUSTRALIA:	BUTTERWORTH & CO. (AUSTRALIA) LTD. SYDNEY: 20 Loftus Street MELBOURNE: 343 Little Collins Street BRISBANE: 240 Queen Street
CANADA:	BUTTERWORTH & CO. (CANADA) LTD. TORONTO: 14 Curity Avenue, 16
NEW ZEALAND:	BUTTERWORTH & CO. (NEW ZEALAND) LTD. WELLINGTON: 49/51 Ballance Street AUCKLAND: 35 High Street
SOUTH AFRICA:	BUTTERWORTH & CO. (SOUTH AFRICA) LTD. DURBAN: 33/35 Beach Grove

First printed 1962
Reprinted with revisions 1964
Reprinted 1968

Suggested U.D.C. *number* 541·124

©
Butterworth & Co. (Publishers) Ltd.

1962

Printed in Great Britain by Page Bros. (*Norwich*) *Ltd.*

CONTENTS

PREFACE

The object of this book is to provide a short introduction to the main ideas of chemical reaction kinetics. It is intended for students reading the subject for the first time, in particular, for those taking Higher National Certificates or the Part I examination of the Royal Institute of Chemistry. It should also be useful for first-year honours students, in providing a less rigorous introduction to the subject than is found in the conventional text-book.

Particular attention has been paid to the explanation of mathematical working, and all the mathematical results used have been listed in an appendix to which reference is frequently made.

The usefulness of kinetic studies in chemistry is sometimes difficult to see from a formal study of the subject. For this reason, a chapter has been included which gives examples of reactions whose mechanisms have been investigated by simple kinetic methods. This should enable even elementary classes to see that a study of kinetics is more than just a theoretical exercise.

Although a study of heterogeneous and chain reactions is not found in all Higher National Certificate schemes, chapters on these topics have been added to illustrate the application of kinetic ideas to reactions of vital industrial importance.

Finally, a chapter on worked examples, rather than problems for the student to attempt himself, has been included to demonstrate in detail the numerical techniques involved in kinetic calculations.

INTRODUCTION

The subject of reaction kinetics is concerned with the detailed study of the rates of chemical reactions. The experimental part of the subject deals with ways of measuring precisely the rates of reactions at various temperatures. The interpretation of the results leads to an understanding of the mechanism of reactions. The combination of the results of a large number of experiments give rise to general theories of chemical reactivity.

From a scientific point of view there are two important things about a process of change. The first is the ultimate result of the change; the second is the time taken for this ultimate result to be attained. It is no consolation to the master of ship, which has struck an iceberg, to be told that if only he had waited a few years for equilibrium to be reached, the iceberg would have melted and the ship would have been safe!

In chemical reactions, the problem of predicting the products when equilibrium is eventually reached is dealt with in chemical thermodynamics[1] in which it is shown that the equilibrium constant can be predicted from free energies obtained from measurements made in a calorimeter. When equilibrium is achieved rapidly, it is possible to predict quite accurately the products of reaction in simple cases. Thermodynamics has, however, nothing to say about the *rate* at which a chemical reaction will occur. An analogy may be drawn with the case of a stone falling under gravity. Knowledge that its ultimate position will be on the ground (a 'thermodynamic' result) enables no deductions to be made about the rate of fall.

---

[1] 'Elementary Chemical Thermodynamics', G. Hargreaves, Butterworths, 1961.

The inadequacy of the thermodynamic approach is seen by considering the reaction of hydrogen and oxygen at one atmosphere pressure and room temperature. The reaction appears to occur instantaneously when the mixture is sparked. On the other hand, in the absence of a spark or a catalyst, no reaction is detectable after several years. Thermodynamic calculations show, however, that the reaction is accompanied by a large decrease in free energy, and so should be capable of occurring spontaneously with some vigour. The kinetic explanation of these results is discussed in Chapter 9.

There are many examples of chemical reactions that occur at a measurable rate. It is worth noting that the process of life itself depends on the combined effect of many thousands of chemical reactions, each proceeding at a steady rate at body temperature. The dramatic effect of temperature on rate of reaction (see Chapter 4) is illustrated by the fact that a 10°C rise in temperature of the human body invariably leads to death.

Before proceeding further it is necessary to note that many of the technical terms used in describing reaction kinetics (e.g. 'rate' and 'order'), are also used ordinarily in a non-kinetic sense. For this reason, Chapter 1 lists and explains some of the special terms used. It is intended to serve as a convenient summary of definitions of the more important kinetic terms.

To deal with the fact that the rates of chemical reactions vary continuously with time, it is necessary to have some knowledge of the mathematical technique specially devised to deal with continuously varying quantities—namely infinitesimal calculus.

To help the reader who cannot readily bring to mind the mathematical results used in this book, an appendix has been included in which all the mathematical results used are listed and numbered. Where these results are used in the text they are referred to by the letter M (for Mathematical Appendix) followed by the number of the result in the appendix. Thus M17 would refer to the seventeenth result quoted in the appendix, i.e.

M17 $\qquad \ln x = 2 \cdot 303 \log x.$

The equations in the book are numbered according to the Chapter. Thus (2.11) refers to the eleventh numbered equation in Chapter 2.

The principal equations developed in the text are placed in a rectangular box on the first occasion on which they occur. This has been done to help the reader pick out the important points that should be committed to memory.

A complete list of symbols has also been included on page 114.

LAW OF MASS ACTION

The first kinetic study of a chemical reaction was carried out in 1850 by Wilhelmy who measured the rate of conversion of an acidic solution of sucrose into glucose and fructose. This reaction was especially suitable for kinetic study as the amount of reaction could be found at any time by measuring the optical rotation of the solution in a polarimeter. Wilhelmy found that, at a given concentration of acid, the rate of reaction at any instant was proportional to the amount of sucrose remaining in solution.

In 1862, Berthelot and St. Gilles made a careful study of the equilibrium between acetic acid, ethanol, ethyl acetate and water.

$$CH_3COOH + C_2H_5OH \rightleftharpoons CH_3COOC_2H_5 + H_2O$$

They were able to show that in this reversible reaction the rate of the forward reaction was proportional to the concentration of ethanol multiplied by the concentration of acetic acid.

The idea that the rate of a chemical reaction at a given temperature depends on concentration was generalized by Guldberg and Waage who, in 1863, stated the *Law of Mass Action*. In modern terms this states that the rate of a chemical reaction is proportional to the concentration of each reactant. This law provides a quantitative basis for kinetic investigations.

One point that may cause confusion is that the Law of Mass Action is defined in some text-books in terms of 'active mass'. This is for historical reasons as Guldberg and Waage used it in their original publication. The term 'active mass' has, however, no connection with the thermo-dynamic concept of 'activity'. In fact the rates of chemical reactions are proportional to the concentrations of the reagents rather than to their activities. To avoid confusion it is best to state the Law of Mass Action in terms of concentration. The concentration of a gas is measured by its pressure.

Guldberg and Waage further showed that the position of chemical equilibrium can be explained quantitatively for a reversible reaction by assuming a *dynamic* rather than a *static* equilibrium. Hence the rate of the forward reaction is equal to the rate of the back reaction. Thus consider the reversible reaction

$$A + B \rightleftharpoons C + D$$

Using the idea of a dynamic equilibrium,

rate of forward reaction = rate of back reaction

From the Law of Mass Action these rates are proportional to the products of the concentrations of the reactants i.e., using M1,

$$k_f ab = k_b cd$$

where a, b, c, d represent the concentrations of A, B, C, D.

k_f and k_b are proportionality constants.

Re-arranging this equation

$$\boxed{\frac{cd}{ab} = \frac{k_f}{k_b} = K}$$

since the ratio of the two constants is also a constant (K). The above equation is a mathematical expression for a simple equilibrium constant.

In *one-stage reactions* the law of mass action may be applied directly to the concentrations of the reactants. If, however, a reaction occurs in a series of consecutive stages, the law must be applied successively to each individual stage of the reaction.

The Law of Mass Action may be given a molecular interpretation when applied to a reaction of the type

$$A + B \rightarrow \text{products}$$

in which one molecule of A reacts with one molecule of B. Before the two molecules can react with one another to form a compound they must first meet. The number of collisions between the molecules of A and of B on simple probability theory is proportional to the number of molecules of A multiplied by the number of molecules of B, which in turn is proportional to the concentration of A multiplied by the concentration of B. The Law of Mass Action thus follows from the reasonable assumption that the number of molecules of A and B that react is proportional to the number of collisions between them.

EXPLANATION OF KINETIC TERMS

The purpose of this chapter is to introduce the main concepts in reaction kinetics in such a way that they can be easily referred to later. These terms are used and explained in more detail in the subsequent chapters.

Chemical reactions can be divided into two broad categories—*homogeneous* and *heterogeneous*. In the former case only one phase is present and the system is uniform in composition throughout. Reactions in a single solvent in which no solid catalyst is used are homogeneous. So, too, are gas reactions that do not involve catalysts or free radicals. Some examples of homogeneous reactions are

$$H_2 + I_2 \rightarrow 2HI \text{ (in the gas phase)}$$
$$CH_3COCl + CH_3OH \rightarrow CH_3CO \cdot OCH_3 + HCl \text{ (in the liquid phase)}$$

In heterogeneous reactions the mixture is not uniform throughout, and reaction occurs at phase boundaries. This is typically the case when solid catalysts are used as in the following examples:

$$C_2H_5OH \xrightarrow{\text{alumina}} C_2H_4 + H_2O$$
$$2NH_3 \xrightarrow{\text{tungsten}} N_2 + 3H_2$$

Homogeneous reactions are the most common type studied and these are dealt with first in this book. Heterogeneous reactions are considered to some extent in Chapter 8.

RATE OF REACTION

The precise meaning of the term 'rate of reaction' is not self-evident. A simple definition would be the mass of product formed in a given time under stated conditions. There are, however, two objections to this interpretation:

(a) the concentration of reactants changes as the reaction proceeds, and hence constant conditions cannot be maintained;

(b) the amount of product formed depends on the initial quantity of reactants as well as on their concentrations and chemical reactivities.

These difficulties are overcome by defining the rate of reaction as the decrease in concentration per unit time of one of the reactants. Concentrations are usually expressed in moles per litre; the time in minutes or seconds.

This definition may be expressed more concisely using the notation of the differential calculus.

If [A] represents the concentration of the reactant A, measured at time t, then the rate is defined as

$$\text{rate} = -\,d\,[A]/dt \qquad\qquad 1.1$$

The minus sign occurs because the concentration of the reactant *decreases* with increasing time. An alternative definition of the rate of reaction is in terms of the product. If a represents the initial concentration of A and x represents the concentration of product at time t then

$$\text{rate} = +\,dx/dt \qquad\qquad 1.2$$

or

$$\text{rate} = \frac{-\,d(a-x)}{dt} \qquad\qquad 1.3$$

in (1.2) the sign is positive since the concentration of products *increases* with time (see M18).

A typical curve of percentage reaction plotted against time is shown in FIGURE 1. It illustrates two general features of chemical kinetics. The first is that the amount of reaction in a given time interval decreases as the reaction proceeds.

2

The amounts of reaction for two equal time intervals are shown on the graph. AB, which corresponds to the earlier time, is much greater than CD. The rate of reaction, using (1.2) is the slope of the curve, which clearly decreases with increasing time.

The second point is that there is no definite instant of time at which the reaction is completed, as the curve approaches 100 per cent reaction asymptotically.

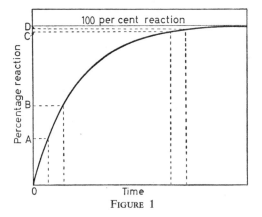

FIGURE 1

RATE CONSTANT

(Alternative names are rate coefficient or specific reaction rate. Usual symbol is k)

The rate constant is a measure of the rate of a given chemical reaction under specified conditions. It may be defined in words as the change in concentration of reactant or product per unit time in a reaction in which all the reactants are at unit concentration. The definition is helpful in that it gives some physical meaning to the rate constant. But it cannot always be used quantitatively because:

(a) chemical reactions are not, in general, carried out with all the reagents at one mole per litre; indeed many reagents are not soluble to this extent.

(b) even if the system were initially at unit concentration, as soon as reaction occurred the concentrations would alter. Hence the definition is valid only where the amount of reaction in unit time is small.

As an example, in the decomposition of benzene diazonium chloride in water

$$C_6H_5N_2Cl + H_2O \rightarrow C_6H_5OH + N_2 + HCl$$

the rate constant is $4 \cdot 24 \times 10^{-4}$ sec^{-1} at $40 \cdot 0°C$. From the definition, in one litre of a one molar solution, $4 \cdot 24 \times 10^{-4}$ moles of benzene diazonium chloride will react in one second at this temperature. It follows also that if the unit of time used in measuring the rate constant is changed from seconds to minutes, the rate constant will increase by a factor of sixty.

In order to obtain a precise definition, applicable to all cases, the calculus notation must be used.

At constant temperature the rate of reaction depends upon the concentrations of the reactants, although it is not always directly proportional to them as would be implied by the law of mass action. In more formal language:
rate of reaction $=$ a constant times a function of concentrations of reactants

$$dx/dt = k \cdot f(a, b, c, \ldots) \tag{1.4}$$

where k is the rate constant and a, b, c, . . . represent the concentrations of the reactants A, B, C, . . . at time t. The function $f(a, b, c, \ldots)$ represents some mathematical expression that is a characteristic of the reaction. This function only involves the concentrations, each raised to a certain power and so it becomes unity when all the reactants are at unit concentration since $1^n = 1$. Under these conditions, therefore, $dx/dt = k$, which is the rate constant in agreement with the earlier definition.

For a given reaction, the value of k is constant at a constant temperature, and is a convenient quantitative measure of chemical reactivity. It must be stressed, however, that k increases rapidly with temperature, and so equations like (1.4) are only valid when the temperature is kept constant.

RATE LAW

An equation like (1.4) which relates the rate of reaction to the concentrations of reactants is called the rate law or the rate equation. It is determined by experiment (see Chapter 2 page 19). In simple reactions the rate law takes one of the following forms:

$$\frac{\mathrm{d}x}{\mathrm{d}t} = k \qquad\qquad 1.5$$

$$\frac{\mathrm{d}x}{\mathrm{d}t} = k(a - x) \qquad\qquad 1.6$$

$$\frac{\mathrm{d}x}{\mathrm{d}t} = k(a - x)^2 \qquad\qquad 1.7$$

$$\frac{\mathrm{d}x}{\mathrm{d}t} = k(a - x)(b - x) \qquad\qquad 1.8$$

$$\frac{\mathrm{d}x}{\mathrm{d}t} = k(a - x)(b - x)^2 \qquad\qquad 1.9$$

In complex reactions the rate law often takes a more elaborate form and fractional powers may occur.

The rate laws (1.4) to (1.9) are differential equations and are referred to as the differential form of the rate law. They may be integrated (see Chapter 2) to give the rate law in a form into which experimental results may be substituted directly. The result of the integration is referred to as the integrated form of the rate law.

ORDER OF REACTION

The term 'order of reaction' is used to classify the various types of rate law. The order is usually a small whole number, but in special cases it may have a fractional value or be zero. It is formally defined as the sum of the powers of the concentration terms that occur in the differential form of the rate law. Thus a reaction with rate law (1.6) is first order since one concentration term occurs in the rate law. (1.7) and (1.8) are second order and (1.9) is third order. Since any number to the power of zero equals one, (1.5) may be written $dx/dt = k(a - x)^0$ and is therefore of zero order (see M6).

It cannot be too strongly emphasized that the order of reaction is entirely an experimental quantity. It can be measured experimentally without any prior knowledge of the mechanism of the reaction. This follows from the fact that the order is determined by finding out which rate law best fits the experimental data. The order can *not* be found by looking at the chemical equation for the reaction. Finally, it must not be confused with molecularity which is defined below.

MOLECULARITY OF REACTION

The strength of a chain cannot exceed the strength of the weakest link. There is a corresponding principle in kinetics, namely that the overall rate of a process cannot exceed the rate of the slowest stage. This 'bottleneck principle' is frequently observed in everyday life. For instance, if a large crowd is leaving a building which has only a few small exits (such as a theatre or cinema), the time taken to empty the building is determined by the number of people who can squeeze through the doors per second. Whether people run or walk to the doors makes no difference to the rate of leaving; it merely affects the size of the queue inside.

If a chemical reaction has more than one consecutive stage, then the kinetics are limited by the slowest stage, which is 'rate determining'. The molecularity of a reaction is defined as the number of molecules or ions that participate in the rate determining stage.

The molecularity is a theoretical quantity in that to evaluate it the mechanism of reaction must be known or assumed.

In contrast to the order, the molecularity is necessarily a small whole number and cannot be zero or fractional. The terms 'unimolecular' and 'bimolecular' are used to describe reactions which have a molecularity of one and two respectively.

In many cases the order and molecularity are equal, for example bimolecular reactions are usually of second order if the reaction occurs in one stage.

Thus the thermal decomposition of hydrogen iodide

$$2HI \rightarrow H_2 + I_2$$

is a second order bimolecular reaction, and the thermal decomposition of tertiary butyl alcohol

$$t\text{-}C_4H_9OH \rightarrow C_4H_8 + H_2O$$

is a first order unimolecular reaction. On the other hand, the reaction of iodine with acidified acetone

$$CH_3COCH_3 + I_2 \rightarrow CH_3COCH_2I + HI$$

is bimolecular and of zero order (see page 62). The oxidation of nitric oxide

$$2NO + O_2 \rightarrow 2NO_2$$

is bimolecular and of third order (see page 67).

It should be noted that some of the older text-books on kinetics do not distinguish clearly between order and molecularity and refer indiscriminately to second order reactions as 'bimolecular'.

HALF-LIFE
(symbol $t_{\frac{1}{2}}$)

In some cases it is convenient to define the rate of a chemical reaction by stating the time taken for 50 per cent reaction to occur. This time is called the half-life. It is widely used in describing the rates of radioactive decay in which the half-life is independent of the amount of material present (see equation 2.11). In general the half-life depends upon the initial concentrations as well as upon the rate constant.

INFINITE TIME

Chemical reactions approach completion gradually (see FIGURE 1) and so there is no instant of time at which the reaction finishes. However, it is often necessary to know what the final concentrations of the reactants will be. By 'infinite time' is meant the time at which the reaction is complete for all practical purposes (say more than 99·9 per cent reaction). Thus one can tell experimentally when 'infinite time' has been reached by the constancy of the composition of the reaction mixture.

In first order reactions, infinite time may be taken as ten times the half-life. In second order reactions a considerably longer period is needed. In many cases the time taken to reach 99·9 per cent reaction can be conveniently reduced by warming a sample of the reaction mixture. This technique is often used when it is necessary to know the concentrations of the reactants at infinite time in order to calculate the rate constant.

It should be noted that the word 'infinite' is used in this context in a relative sense, and that infinite time can vary from a fraction of a second to many years depending on the reaction.

INTEGRATION OF THE RATE LAWS

The main problem dealt with in this chapter is that of converting the rate laws into a form from which the rate constant and order of reaction can be calculated. As mentioned in the definitions in equations (1.5) to (1.9), the rate laws for the different orders of reaction are differential equations since they all involve the term dx/dt for the rate of reaction (where x represents the concentration of product formed or reactant consumed at time t).

In practice dx/dt cannot be measured directly, since the result of analyses at various times will be to give a series of values of concentration (x) corresponding to various times (t). There are, however, two methods that might be employed to derive the rate constant of the reaction.

The first method is to plot a graph of x against t and measure the slope of the curve at various values of x. This gives dx/dt (see M18) which can then be substituted directly into the rate law to give the rate constant. For example, if the rate law is $dx/dt = k(a - x)$

$$\text{then } k = \frac{dx/dt}{(a - x)} \qquad 2.1$$

This method of calculation is used in Chapter 10, Example 1.

The objection to the general use of this method, which is mathematically simple, is that it lacks in accuracy because of the difficulty of measuring the slope of a curve. This difficulty is accentuated if the curve is not completely smooth due to experimental errors in some of the points.

The numerical measurement of the slope of the curve is avoided, in the second method, by integrating the rate equation before the experimental results are substituted into it. This converts the rate law from the differential form to an equation of the type

$$kt = \text{function of } x = F(x), \text{ say} \qquad 2.2$$

Using the function $F(x)$ derived below for the appropriate order of reaction, k can be found directly by substituting values of x and t into it.

Small experimental errors can be dealt with by plotting a graph of $F(x)$ against t and (either visually, or by the method of least squares) drawing the best straight line through the origin and the points. Using M3, the slope of the line is equal to k.

ZERO ORDER REACTIONS

These reactions are not common, but they do occur in some cases in heterogeneous systems (page 79) and in solutions (page 62). The appropriate rate law for a zero order reaction is

$$\text{rate} = \text{constant}$$

or, in mathematical symbols,

$$\boxed{\frac{\mathrm{d}x}{\mathrm{d}t} = k} \qquad 2.3$$

Integrating with respect to t (using M20)

$$x = kt + \text{constant}$$

Since $x = 0$ when $t = 0$ (i.e. at the beginning of the reaction, no product has formed) the constant must be zero. Hence

$$\boxed{x = kt} \qquad 2.4$$

The dimensions of k are concentration/time, i.e. mole litre^{-1} sec^{-1}. To calculate the half-life of this reaction the condition that $t = t_{\frac{1}{2}}$ when $x = a/2$ (a being the initial concentration) is substituted into (2.4) to give

$$a/2 = kt_{\frac{1}{2}}$$ 2.5

Thus in a zero order reaction the half-life is proportional to the initial concentration of the reactant.

FIRST ORDER REACTIONS

These reactions are common and are observed in solution where the solvent happens to be one of the reactants. Many gas phase reactions, and radioactive decay also obey the first order rate law

$$\frac{\mathrm{d}x}{\mathrm{d}t} = k(a - x)$$ 2.6

Rearrangement gives

$$\frac{\mathrm{d}x}{(a - x)} = k \cdot \mathrm{d}t$$ 2.7

Integrating (2.7) using M21,

$$- \ln (a - x) = kt + \text{constant.}$$ 2.8

When $t = 0$, $x = 0$ and hence $- \ln a = \text{constant}$. Substituting for the constant in (2.8)

$$\ln a - \ln (a - x) = kt$$ 2.9

or, using M14,

$$kt = \ln \frac{a}{a - x}$$ 2.10

It will be seen from (2.10) that the value of k depends only on the *ratio* of two concentrations, the dimensions of k being 1/time, i.e. $\sec^{-1}$. The important practical point that

11

follows from this is that the first order rate constant can be calculated from the relative values of the concentrations at various times (see M16). Thus the first order reaction

$$RBr + C_2H_5OH \rightarrow ROC_2H_5 + HBr$$

(where R is an alkyl group) can be followed by removing aliquots, cooling them rapidly and titrating the liberated HBr with alkali. The strength of the alkali is not needed in order to find k, since the ratio $a/(a - x)$ which is required in (2.10) can be expressed as the ratio of two titrations. If T_∞ is the titration after 'infinite' time and T is the titration after time t then

$$\frac{a}{a - x} = \frac{T_\infty}{T_\infty - T}$$

The use of this type of calculation is shown in Chapter 10, Example 2.

First order reactions have another important property which is that the half-life (i.e. the time for 50 per cent reaction) does not depend on the initial concentration. This may be seen by substituting in (2.10) the conditions for the half-life, namely that when $t = t_{\frac{1}{2}}$, $x = a/2$. Whence

$$\ln 2 = kt_{\frac{1}{2}}$$

i.e.
$$t_{\frac{1}{2}} = \frac{\ln 2}{k} = \frac{0 \cdot 6932}{k}$$

2.11

The half-life is thus independent of the initial concentration of the reactants. In other words, provided a reaction obeys strictly the first order equation, the time for 50 per cent reaction cannot be changed by altering the initial concentrations. For batch processes this means that the batch time cannot be decreased by increasing the concentration of the reactants.

For first order reactions the half-life is directly related to the rate constant by an expression (2.11) that is independent of the initial concentration. The half-life is an easier concept to visualize than a rate constant, and so in the case of radio-active decay, where the processes are all first order, rates are expressed in terms of half-lives. Thus the statement that the half-life of radium is 1690 years means that its first order rate constant is $\ln 2/1690$ years^{-1} = $1\cdot301 \times 10^{-11}$ sec^{-1}. Unfortunately, in all chemical reactions with order other than unity the half-life depends on the initial con-centration. In order to be consistent it is preferable to use rate constants for all orders of reaction.

SECOND ORDER REACTIONS

This is the most common order of reaction and in general it may be said that, provided a reaction occurs in a single step and the reactants are present in roughly equal con-centrations, a second order reaction may be expected. Reactions of this type occur often in organic chemistry.
A simple second order reaction is

$$A + B \rightarrow products$$

in which one molecule of A reacts with one molecule of B. If x denotes the decrease in concentration of A and B at time t, the rate law states that the rate is proportional to the concentration of both reactants, i.e.

$$\frac{dx}{dt} = k(a - x)(b - x)$$

2.12

First consider the special case in which the initial concentra-tions of A and B are equal. (2.12) then becomes

$$\frac{dx}{dt} = k(a - x)^2$$

2.13

Rearranging

$$\frac{dx}{(a - x)^2} = k \cdot dt$$

13

Integrating using M20,

$$\frac{1}{(a-x)} = kt + \text{constant} \qquad 2.14$$

$x = 0$ when $t = 0$, whence $1/a = \text{constant}$.

Substituting for the constant in (2.14)

$$kt = \frac{1}{(a-x)} - \frac{1}{a}$$

i.e.

$$kt = \frac{x}{a(a-x)} \qquad 2.15$$

To evaluate graphically the rate constant of a second order reaction (with equal concentrations of reactants) a graph is plotted of $x/(a-x)$ against time when a straight line through the origin is obtained with slope equal to ak. As in the case of first order reactions, the fraction $x/(a-x)$, which is required for the graph, may be expressed as a ratio of concentrations. But the absolute value of the initial concentration is required to convert the slope of the graph into the rate constant. A numerical example of this type of calculation is shown in Chapter 10, example 3.

The half-life can be found by substituting the usual condition that $t = t_{\frac{1}{2}}$ when $x = a/2$ into the integrated rate equation (2.15).

This gives

$$kt_{\frac{1}{2}} = \frac{1}{a}$$

i.e.

$$t_{\frac{1}{2}} = \frac{1}{ka} \qquad 2.16$$

Thus, in contrast to the result for first order reactions (2.11), the half-life of a second order reaction is inversely proportional to the initial concentration of reactants, i.e.

increasing the concentration will decrease the time taken to reach 50 per cent reaction.

In dealing with second order reactions in which the initial concentrations are not equal, the half-life must be expressed relative to one of the reactants, and it is not possible to derive a simple expression for half-life in terms of initial concentration and rate constant. Nevertheless it is still true to say that an increase in initial concentration will decrease the time for a given amount of reaction.

The general form of the second order rate law is

$$\frac{dx}{dt} = k(a - x)(b - x) \qquad \text{2.17}$$

which may be integrated as follows:
Re-arranging (2.17)

$$\frac{dx}{(a - x)(b - x)} = k \cdot dt \qquad \text{2.18}$$

Re-arranging (2.18), using partial fractions, gives

$$\frac{1}{a - b}\left[\frac{1}{b - x} - \frac{1}{a - x}\right] dx = k \cdot dt \qquad \text{2.19}$$

which on integrating (using M21) gives

$$(a - b)\,kt = \ln(a - x) - \ln(b - x) + \text{constant.} \qquad \text{2.20}$$

Using the condition that $x = 0$, when $t = 0$, and M14,

$$\text{constant} = \ln\frac{b}{a} \qquad \text{2.21}$$

Substituting (2.21) in (2.20) and re-arranging

$$(a - b)\,kt = \ln\frac{b(a - x)}{a(b - x)} \qquad \text{2.22}$$

k may be evaluated from (2.22) by plotting a graph of $\ln[(a - x)/(b - x)]$ against time when a straight line passing through the origin with slope equal to $(a - b)k$ is obtained. A numerical example of the use of (2.22) is given in Chapter 10, Example 4.

In many cases it is not possible to ensure that the initial concentrations of a and b are equal. (2.22) must then be used.

It sometimes happens in a second order reaction that more than one molecule of one reactant (A) is consumed for each molecule of B as in the reaction

$$2A + B \rightarrow \text{products}$$

In this case, if x represents the change in concentration of B the rate law becomes

$$\frac{dx}{dt} = k(a - 2x)(b - x) \qquad 2.23$$

the integrated form of which is

$$(a - 2b)kt = \ln \frac{b\,(a - 2x)}{a\,(b - x)} \qquad 2.24$$

A bimolecular second order reaction that obeys this rate law is the reaction of 2,4-dinitrochlorobenzene with aniline in benzene. Denoting the first compound as RCl the reaction occurs as follows:

$$\text{RCl} + \text{C}_6\text{H}_5\text{NH}_2 \rightarrow \text{C}_6\text{H}_5\text{NHR} + \text{HCl}$$

$$\text{HCl} + \text{C}_6\text{H}_5\text{NH}_2 \rightarrow \text{C}_6\text{H}_5\text{NH}_3\text{Cl} \text{ (aniline hydrochloride)}$$

The aniline hydrochloride does not react with the 2:4 dinitrochlorobenzene, and so for each molecule of the latter that reacts two molecules of aniline are removed. Thus the modified rate law (2.24) is obeyed.

THIRD ORDER REACTIONS

Reactions of this order are rare, the few well established cases being concerned with the reactions of nitric oxide. Termolecular reactions are theoretically expected to be uncommon since the probability of a collision involving three molecules with sufficient energy to react and with correct orientations is very slight.

In the simple case of a third order reaction in which all the reactants are at the same initial concentration a the rate law becomes

$$\frac{dx}{dt} = k(a - x)^3 \qquad 2.25$$

Rearranging

$$\frac{dx}{(a - x)^3} = k \cdot dt \qquad 2.26$$

Integrating (2.26) using M20,

$$\frac{1}{2(a - x)^2} = kt + \text{constant} \qquad 2.27$$

At the beginning of the reaction $x = 0$ when $t = 0$.

Thus, $$\text{constant} = \frac{1}{2a^2}$$

Hence from (2.27)

$$kt = \frac{1}{2(a - x)^2} - \frac{1}{2a^2} \qquad 2.28$$

The half-life can be found by substituting the condition

$$x = \frac{a}{2} \text{ when } t = t_{\frac{1}{2}} \text{ in (2.28)}$$

This gives

$$kt_{\frac{1}{2}} = \frac{3}{2a^2} \qquad 2.29$$

The half-life is therefore inversely proportional to the square of the initial concentration.

Comparison of (2.5), (2.11), (2.16) and (2.29) shows that the dependence of half-life on concentration varies in a regular way as the order is changed. This is shown, together with a summary of the main points in this chapter, in the table overleaf.

TABLE 1

Order	Rate law in differential form	Rate law in integrated form	Dimensions of k	Half-life proportional to
0	$\dfrac{dx}{dt} = k$	$kt = x$	mole litre^{-1} sec^{-1}	a^1
1	$\dfrac{dx}{dt} = k(a-x)$	$kt = \ln\dfrac{a}{(a-x)}$	sec^{-1}	$a^0 (= 1)$
2	$\dfrac{dx}{dt} = k(a-x)^2$	$kt = \dfrac{x}{a(a-x)}$	litre mole^{-1} sec^{-1}	a^{-1}
3	$\dfrac{dx}{dt} = k(a-x)^3$	$kt = \dfrac{1}{2(a-x)^2} - \dfrac{1}{2a^2}$	litre^2 mole^{-2} sec^{-1}	a^{-2}
2	$\dfrac{dx}{dt} = k(a-x)(b-x)$	$kt = \dfrac{1}{a-b}\ln\dfrac{b(a-x)}{a(b-x)}$	litre mole^{-1} sec^{-1}	—

18

DETERMINATION OF ORDER OF REACTION

The two most convenient methods of determining the order of a reaction from the experimental results are:

(a) *The method of empirical fit*

It is assumed that experimental data are available in the form of a series of values of x at various values of time, including the initial value when $t = 0$. These data are all substituted into each of the rate laws in turn until a law is found that gives constant values of k, or that gives a straight line plot when the appropriate function of x is plotted against time. Thus, if it is suspected that a reaction is of the first order, a graph of $\log (a - x)$ against time is plotted. If the result is a straight line the reaction is in fact first order. If the results do not, however, fit the first order law, they must be substituted into the other rate equations until one is found that gives a constant value of k.

This procedure is illustrated in FIGURE 2, in which data, calculated to fit a second order rate law, have been plotted in turn according to the zero, first and second order laws. The initial concentrations of the two reactants are 0.100 mole litre^{-1}. The value of k from the slope of the straight line graph (using (2.15)) is 2.18×10^{-3} litre mole^{-1} sec^{-1}.

It will be seen that over a small fraction of the reaction the plots for the various orders are nearly linear. Hence to establish the order by this method it is essential to follow the kinetics over as large a fraction of the reaction as possible.

(b) *The half-life method*

This method involves measuring the rate of a reaction several times at the same temperature, varying the initial concentration of the reactants. To simplify the mathematical treatment, all reactants used are made up initially at the same concentration so that one of the first four rate laws in TABLE 1 applies. From the experimental results, a graph of percentage reaction against time is plotted, and by inter-polation the times for 50 per cent reaction (half-life) are found. By combining the results in TABLE 1, it is seen that if n equals the order of reaction, then the half-life of a given order of reaction is given by the equation

$$t_{\frac{1}{2}} \propto a^{1-n}$$

(using M1) $\qquad t_{\frac{1}{2}} = Ca^{1-n}$ 2.30

where C is a proportionality constant.

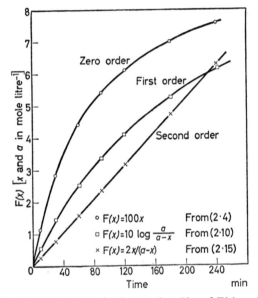

FIGURE 2. Determination of order reaction. Plot of F(x) against time for zero, first and second order rate laws

Taking logarithms of (2.30) (using M13)

$$\log t_{\frac{1}{2}} = \log C + (1 - n) \log a$$ 2.31

Thus, if a graph of the logarithm of the half-life is plotted against the logarithm of the initial concentration, a straight line will be obtained with a slope of 1, 0, -1 and -2 for zero, first, second and third order reactions respectively. If a straight line is not obtained in this plot, the kinetics are governed by more complicated equations than those in TABLE 1 (e.g. fractional orders or consecutive reactions). The half-life method is more reliable than the method of empirical fit, but it involves far more experimental work.

3

EXPERIMENTAL METHODS

This chapter is concerned with the experimental techniques required to measure reaction rates and rate constants. Details of the numerical calculations involved are shown in the worked examples of Chapter 10.

In essence the experimental problem in reaction kinetics is to devise an analytical technique, together with suitable sampling methods, if necessary, to enable the concentration of one of the reactants to be measured at any time during a reaction occurring at constant temperature. When using the sampling technique it must be possible to 'freeze' the reaction in the sample so that in the time taken to carry out the analysis no further product is formed. For reactions at high temperatures this may be done by cooling, but for reactions occurring near room temperature one of the reactants must be removed chemically. Thus an acid-catalysed reaction may be 'frozen' by running the sample into a solution containing excess alkali.

The initial concentrations of the reactants are most accurately determined by weighing a known amount of substance directly into a volumetric flask and making up to the mark with the appropriate solvent. Alternatively, a solution of approximately known concentration may be prepared, and an aliquot of this removed and analysed by one of the usual volumetric techniques.

The rates of chemical reactions vary markedly with temperature and as a rough working rule a 5 per cent to 10 per cent increase in rate per degree centigrade rise in temperature may be assumed. Hence to obtain rate constants to an accuracy of 2 per cent the temperature must be held constant to within 0·1°C. Hence the first requirement for kinetic studies is a bath fitted with an accurate means of controlling the temperature. Many commercial control units are available that are suitable for kinetic work.

It should be stressed, however, that if a large bath is used with only one stirrer there may be temperature gradients in the bath. This can be checked by measuring the temperature at several points with a Beckmann thermometer. The temperature of the bath should be measured with a thermometer that has been compared with a National Physical Laboratories standard.

A laboratory stop-clock is sufficiently accurate for measuring the time of reaction, since an error as large as a quarter of an hour per day is equivalent to only a one per cent error in the time measurement.

At high temperatures, an appreciable amount of reaction can occur in the time taken to reach bath temperature from room temperature, so the experiment must be started with particular care. The usual procedure is to warm separately solutions of the two reactants until they have reached the bath temperature. They are then rapidly mixed and stirred and an aliquot is removed immediately before the clock is started. The time at which the clock is started is known as 'zero time'. The concentrations of the reactants at 'zero time' can then be calculated from the titration of the first aliquot removed.

A further complication in reactions at high temperatures is due to the expansion of the solvent which lowers the concentration of the solution. For accurate work this expansion must be allowed for (see Chapter 10, example 4).

Several common methods of analysis used in kinetic studies are listed below together with some comments on their applicability.

SAMPLING METHODS

There are two main ways of removing samples at known times. In the first, a large volume of the reaction mixture is made up initially and placed in the thermostatted bath. At various times aliquots are withdrawn (e.g. with a pipette previously warmed to the bath temperature). The sample removed is 'frozen' and then analysed, usually by a volumetric method. This sampling method is most frequently used for reactions near room temperature.

For reactions at high temperatures, the vapour pressures of the solvents become appreciable, and to prevent solvent loss, and also for general convenience, the 'sealed tube method' is used. In this a number of aliquots of the reactant mixture, at room temperature, are placed into glass tubes and sealed. These tubes are then all immersed in the thermostatted bath at the same time. After a few minutes, when the tubes have reached bath temperature, one is removed and 'frozen' by cooling and the stop-clock is started. Analysis of the first tube enables the initial concentration to be corrected for the reaction before zero time. The remaining tubes are then removed at suitable times, and analysed. Since the sealed tube technique is used for reactions at high temperatures, simple cooling of the tube in ice water will decrease the rate sufficiently to prevent further reaction taking place while the analysis is carried out. A variation of the sealed tube method is described in Chapter 10, example 3.

A reaction that can be conveniently followed by the first method is the hydrolysis of ethyl acetate by sodium hydroxide in water at 25°C.

$$C_2H_5OCOCH_3 + NaOH \rightarrow CH_3COONa + C_2H_5OH$$

The reaction is followed by removing aliquots and adding them to a known excess of dilute hydrochloric acid which stops the reaction. The excess of acid is then back-titrated with sodium hydroxide.

An appropriate reaction for the sealed tube method is the reaction of sodium ethoxide with n-butyl bromide in ethanol at 60°C.

$$n\text{-}C_4H_9Br + NaOC_2H_5 \rightarrow NaBr + n\text{-}C_4H_5OC_2H_5$$

Here the tubes can be rapidly cooled in an acetone/solid carbon dioxide mixture and then broken under dilute nitric acid. The resultant bromide ions are titrated with standard silver nitrate solution, thus giving the amount of product formed.

Sometimes a sample may be removed and analysed by measuring one of its physical properties. Thus the acid hydrolysis of sucrose to form fructose and glucose can be followed by determining the refractive index of the samples. The kinetics of polymerization reactions are often followed by measuring the increase in viscosity as reaction proceeds. In both cases, however, calibration is necessary to relate the change in the physical property to percentage reaction.

CONTINUOUS METHODS

These methods are based on the measurement of a physical property during the course of a reaction without removing a sample or disturbing the reaction mixture. The following are some of the techniques that have been used in kinetic studies

    (a) electrical conductivity
    (b) optical rotation
    (c) measurement of pressure or volume of gas evolved
    (d) spectrophotometry
    (e) dilatometry

Before using a continuous method, independent chemical analyses should be made to ensure that there is proportionality between the property being measured and the concentration of the reactant. If this is not found to be so, a calibration curve must be drawn which relates the property to be measured to percentage reaction. This curve is then used in interpreting the experimental results.

Electrical Conductivity Method

This is applicable to any reaction involving either an increase or decrease in the number of ions, or the replacement of one ion by another with a different conductivity.

If the solutions are sufficiently dilute it may be assumed that the change in conductivity is proportional to the percentage reaction. A numerical example illustrating this is shown in Chapter 10, example 2. In more concentrated solutions a calibration curve must be prepared.

It may be noted here that the ionic conductivities of the hydrogen and the hydroxyl ions are much larger than the conductivities of other ions. Hence any reaction producing an increase or decrease in the number of these ions will be capable of being followed conductometrically.

Some examples of reactions where this type of technique is applicable are

$$CH_3COOC_2H_5 + NaOH \rightarrow C_2H_5OH + CH_3COONa \qquad 3.1$$

$$t\text{-}C_5H_{11}I + H_2O \rightarrow t\text{-}C_5H_{11}OH + HI \qquad 3.2$$

In (3.1) the conductivity falls with time as the highly conducting hydroxyl ions are converted into acetate ions of lower conductivity. In (3.2) ions are formed in the reaction and so the conductivity increases. In both cases it is necessary to allow the reaction to proceed for 'infinite time' (see page 8) so that the conductivity due to the product may be found.

If C = conductivity at time t

$\quad C°$ = initial conductivity

$\quad C_\infty$ = final conductivity, at 'infinite time'.

Then assuming that change in conductivity is proportional to percentage reaction, amount of reaction at time t is proportional to $C - C°$

Total amount of reaction is proportional to $C_\infty - C°$

$$\therefore \text{Fraction of reaction at time } t = \frac{C - C°}{C_\infty - C°} = \frac{x}{A} \qquad 3.3$$

For a first order reaction, where the rate constant depends only a ratio of concentrations, (3.3) is sufficient to determine the rate constant, as the value of x/A may be substituted into (2.10). A graphical method, as in Chapter 10, example 2, can also be used. For all other orders the initial concentrations must be found by using a known weight of reactant in a known volume of solution.

Optical Rotation Method

In this method the angle through which plane polarized light is rotated by the reaction mixture is measured. It is therefore limited to those reactions involving optically active substances, and has been used extensively in the hydrolysis of sucrose to give glucose and fructose.

The theory of the calculations from optical rotation measurements is the same as that from conductivities given above and so numerical calculations are similar to example 2 of Chapter 10.

If R = rotation at time t

$R°$ = initial rotation

R_∞ = final rotation, then as in the case of the conductivity measurements,

$$\text{fraction of reaction at time } t = \frac{R - R°}{R_\infty - R°} = \frac{x}{A}$$

Reactions Involving Gases

If a gas is liberated in a reaction, the amount of reaction may be conveniently followed by measuring either the volume of gas formed at constant pressure, or the pressure produced by the gas at constant volume. Some examples of reactions which have been followed by this method are

$$C_6H_5N_2Cl + H_2O \xrightarrow{\text{acid}} N_2 + C_6H_5OH + HCl$$
$$CO(CH_2COOH)_2 \xrightarrow{\text{acid}} CO(CH_3)_2 + 2CO_2$$
$$C_2H_5NH_2 \rightarrow C_2H_4 + NH_3$$

It is usual to work at moderately low pressures (up to one atmosphere), and for easily liquefiable gases high temperatures must be used. Under these conditions the perfect gas law can be applied, and the number of gram molecules (n) involved may be calculated using the equation

$$n = pV/RT$$

where p, V, T are the pressure, volume and absolute temperature of the gas, and R is the perfect gas constant.

A typical numerical calculation is given in Chapter 10, example 1.

Spectrophotometry

Spectrophotometry refers to the measurement of the intensity of light transmitted by a solution at various wavelengths. If the product of a chemical reaction absorbs light strongly at a wave length at which the reactants do not absorb, then the reaction can be followed by this method. The spectrophotometer is set to a wave length corresponding to light absorption by the product, and the optical density of the solution is measured at various times.

Dilatometry

In dilatometry the change in volume produced by reaction is measured by placing the reaction mixture in a completely filled reaction vessel connected to a capillary tube. The level of liquid in the capillary is altered if the volume changes. This method is best suited to concentrated solutions where volume changes are greatest. As the dilatometer has essentially the same construction as a thermometer, temperature control to $\pm 0.001\,°C$ is essential. The method has been applied to the hydration of isobutene at 25°C

$$(CH_3)_2C{=}CH_2 + H_2O \xrightarrow{\text{acid}} (CH_3)_3C{\cdot}OH$$

in which there is a small decrease in volume.

It is assumed that the percentage reaction is proportional to percentage movement of the liquid in the capillary.

A range of experiments in chemical reaction kinetics are described in detail in LATHAM, JENKINS and JONES, 'Selected Experiments in Physical Chemistry,' Butterworths, London, 1964.

4

THE EFFECT OF TEMPERATURE ON REACTION RATES—THE ARRHENIUS EQUATION

There is one fundamental problem in reaction kinetics that has not yet been dealt with. From his very first studies the chemist is brought up to believe that all molecules of a given compound are identical (when the existence of isotopes is ignored). Therefore, it would be expected that all molecules of a given compound should behave in the same way in a chemical reaction. But experiment shows that this is not so, for chemical reactions occur at a definite rate, and whereas one molecule may react immediately, another of the same type may have to wait several hours before it can react. In short, 50 per cent of the reacting molecules must wait for more than the half-life before their turn for reaction occurs.

If it is accepted that all molecules of the same compound are equivalent, it might be expected that either no reaction would occur or that every collision between reactant molecules would lead to reaction. In the latter case, calculations show that the frequency of collisions is so high that all reactions would be virtually instantaneous (as in fact is the case for the reaction of hydrogen ions with hydroxyl ions in aqueous solutions). From this viewpoint it is difficult to see how intermediate rates can occur.

Arrhenius solved this problem in 1897 by postulating that normal chemical molecules do not take part in chemical reactions. Only those molecules which possess more than a certain critical energy, called the *energy of activation*, are able to react. The activated molecules are extremely few in number and arise as a result of random collisions between molecules which occasionally give a molecule many times the average energy.

It may be helpful at this point to draw an analogy between the distribution of energy in a molecular system and the distribution of money among men. In both cases the rich are few and the poor are many.

If one imagines that the average income is, say, £600 a year, it will be easily realized that the fraction of the population with an income of more than ten times the average will be relatively small, while the fraction with an income of one hundred times the average (£60,000) will be extremely small but *not* zero.

Accepting this analogy, it will be seen that the activated molecules which possess about twenty times the average energy will be present in very small numbers. So an activated molecule is a rare phenomenon, and the chance of a molecule becoming activated by a single collision is usually much less than the chance that the first stranger that the reader meets will be a millionaire.

It may now be seen why chemical reactions can occur slowly. Even though there may be thousands of millions of collisions per molecule per second, the chance of a molecule becoming an 'energy millionaire' (i.e. activated) is so remote that it may take several minutes, hours or even days before the molecule can react.

This analogy may be taken a stage further. Physiologically, the average man is not significantly different from the £20,000 a year man. But the way of life of the latter is quite different from that of the former. Similarly, an activated molecule does not differ from an average molecule if the energy of activation is removed. But while the molecule possesses this activation energy its chemical reactivity is completely different from that of an average molecule.

It can now be seen why there is no correlation between physical properties and chemical reactivity. The physical properties are determined by all the molecules present, in which the average unactivated molecules play a predominant part. But the average molecules take no part in chemical reactions and so their properties cannot determine chemical reactivity.

Using the idea of activation, Arrhenius derived an equation to describe the variation of rate constant with temperature. This was another puzzling feature of reaction kinetics, for the rates of most reactions at room temperature increase by a factor of two to three for a $10°C$ temperature rise, whereas the kinetic energy of a gas increases by only about 3 per cent for the same temperature rise. This shows that the reaction rate increases much more rapidly than the average energy and hence the average energy cannot be the factor that is determining the rate of reaction.

The original derivation of Arrhenius's equation is as follows. Consider a reversible reaction

$$A + B \rightleftharpoons C + D. \qquad 4.1$$

As shown in the Introduction (page xii) the equilibrium constant (K) of this reaction may be expressed in terms of the rate constants of the forward reaction (k_1) and the back reaction (k_2) by the equation

$$K = \frac{k_1}{k_2} \qquad 4.2$$

It is imagined that when two molecules, which between them possess the activation energy, undergo a collision, they pass into a 'transition' state which is intermediate between the reactants and the products. In FIGURE 3 the heat contents (H) of the reactants, products and transition state are shown diagrammatically. The distance AB corresponds to the difference in energy between the transition state and the reactants, which is the activation energy of the forward reaction (E_1). Similarly BC corresponds to the activation energy of the back reaction (E_2). The heat of reaction (ΔH) is given by AC, and so by the geometrical construction

$$AB - BC = AC$$

or $$E_1 - E_2 = \Delta H$$ 4.3

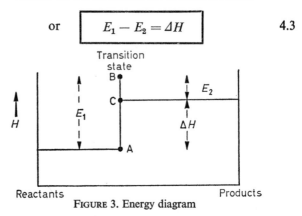

FIGURE 3. Energy diagram

By thermodynamic arguments, it has been shown that the variation of an equilibrium constant (K) with absolute temperature (T) is related to heat of reaction (ΔH) by the equation

$$\frac{\mathrm{d}\ln K}{\mathrm{d}T} = \frac{\Delta H}{RT^2}$$ 4.4

This equation is known as the van't Hoff isochore.
Substituting the kinetic results (4.2) and (4.3) in the thermodynamic equation (4.4) gives

$$\frac{\mathrm{d}}{\mathrm{d}T}\ln\frac{k_1}{k_2} = \frac{E_1 - E_2}{RT^2}$$ 4.5

Re-writing (4.5) using M14

$$\frac{\mathrm{d}\ln k_1}{\mathrm{d}T} - \frac{\mathrm{d}\ln k_2}{\mathrm{d}T} = \frac{E_1}{RT^2} - \frac{E_2}{RT^2}$$ 4.6

An equation of this sort suggests that the forward and back reactions have independent kinetic effects and thus Arrhenius suggested that the equation might be split to give

$$\frac{\mathrm{d}\ln k_1}{\mathrm{d}T} = \frac{E_1}{RT^2} + I \text{ and } \frac{\mathrm{d}\ln k_2}{\mathrm{d}T} = \frac{E_2}{RT^2} + I$$ 4.7

where I is a constant.

Arrhenius found by experiment that the variation of the rate constant (k) with temperature could be expressed satisfactorily by the simplified equation

$$\frac{d \ln k}{dT} = \frac{E}{RT^2}$$

4.8

Equation (4.8) is one form of the Arrhenius equation. It may be integrated using M20 to give

$$\ln k = -E/RT + \text{constant}$$

4.9

assuming that E does not vary with temperature.
Or, using M15,

$$k = A \exp\left(\frac{-E}{RT}\right)$$

4.10

where A is a constant.
(4.8), (4.9) and (4.10) are three equivalent ways of expressing the same equation. It is important that the reader should be able to recognize the Arrhenius equation in any of these three mathematical forms.

An examination of (4.9) shows that E may be determined if the rate constant, or another parameter proportional to it (see M16), is known at several temperatures. For, using M3, a plot of $\ln k$ against the reciprocal of the absolute temperature ($1/T$) gives a straight line of slope $-E/R$. Alternatively, if common logarithms (to the base ten) are used, a plot of $\log k$ against $1/T$ will still be a straight line, but using M17, the slope will be $-E/2 \cdot 303 R$.

The rate constants of many chemical reactions have been measured at several temperatures. In the vast majority of cases the plot of $\log k$ against $1/T$ does in fact give a straight line. This is illustrated by the data in FIGURE 4 which are

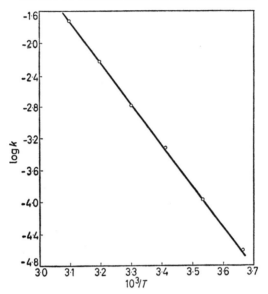

FIGURE 4. Decomposition of acetone dicarboxylic acid in aqueous solution

plotted for the decomposition of acetone dicarboxylic acid in aqueous solution.

$$HOOCCH_2COCH_2COOH \rightarrow CH_3COCH_3 + 2CO_2$$

FIGURE 5 shows the rate constant plotted directly against temperature from the same data.

Examples of the numerical calculations based on the Arrhenius equation are shown in Chapter 10, examples 5 and 6.

If the values of the rate constant at two temperatures T_1 and T_2 are k_1 and k_2 the energy of activation may be obtained from (4.9) by direct substitution

$$\ln k_1 = \frac{-E}{RT_1} + \text{constant} \qquad 4.11$$

34

$$\ln k_2 = \frac{-E}{RT_2} + \text{constant} \qquad 4.12$$

Subtracting (4.12) from (4.11) using M14

$$\boxed{\ln \frac{k_1}{k_2} = -\frac{E}{R}\left[\frac{1}{T_1} - \frac{1}{T_2}\right] = \frac{E}{R}\left[\frac{1}{T_2} - \frac{1}{T_1}\right]} \qquad 4.13$$

Equation (4.13) enables the effect of a 10°C rise in temperature on reaction rate to be calculated. Assume that $E = 20,000$ calories, $T_1 = 37°C$ and $T_2 = 27°C$. $R = 2$ cal mole^{-1}

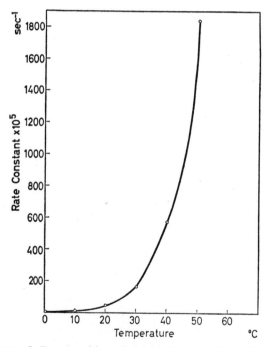

FIGURE 5. Decomposition of acetone dicarboxylic acid in aqueous solution

deg^{-1}. Let k_1 and k_2 refer to the rate constants at 37°C and 27°C respectively.

Then from (4.13)

$$\ln \frac{k_1}{k_2} = \frac{20,000}{2}\left[\frac{1}{300} - \frac{1}{310}\right]$$

$$= \frac{100}{93} = 1\cdot075$$

Taking antilogs from tables of natural logarithms,

$$\frac{k_1}{k_2} = 2\cdot924$$

Thus a 10°C rise in temperature has increased the rate constant by a factor of almost three. It is thus seen that the Arrhenius equation can account for the large effect of temperature on reaction rate already mentioned on page 31.

Examination of the Arrhenius equation in the exponential form (4.10) shows that the constant A has the same dimensions as the rate constant. A is often called the frequency factor and A and E are referred to collectively as the Arrhenius parameters of a chemical reaction. Some values of A and E in various reactions are given in TABLE 2.

TABLE 2.

Reaction	Solvent	E kcal	$\log [A(litre\ mole\ sec^{-1})]$
$CH_3COOC_2H_5 + NaOH \rightarrow$	water	11·3	7·2
$n\text{-}C_5H_{11}Cl + KI \rightarrow$	acetone	18·4	8·0
$C_2H_5ONa + CH_3I \rightarrow$	ethanol	19·5	11·4
$C_2H_5Br + NaOH \rightarrow$	ethanol	21·4	11·6
$NH_4CNO \rightarrow NH_2CONH_2$	water	23·2	12·6
$2N_2O_5 \rightarrow 2N_2O_4 + O_2$	(gas phase)	24·7	13·7
$CH_3I + HI \rightarrow CH_4 + I_2$	(gas phase)	33·4	12·2
$H_2 + I_2 \rightarrow 2HI$	(gas phase)	39·5	11·2
$2HI \rightarrow H_2 + I_2$	(gas phase)	40·0	10·7
$CH_3N_2CH_3 \rightarrow C_2H_6 + N_2$	(gas phase)	52·5	13·5
$CH_2\!\!-\!\!CH_2 \rightarrow CH_3CH\!=\!CH_2$ $\diagdown\ \diagup$ CH_2	(gas phase)	65·0	12·2

In many second order reactions the frequency factor A is about 10^{11} litre mole^{-1} sec^{-1}, i.e. $\log_{10} A$ is roughly 11. The reason for this is discussed in Chapter 5 in considering the theory of reaction rates. Values of the activation energy range from 10 kcal to 50 kcal in most cases. The energy of activation is considerably less than the energy required to break the bond involved in the reaction because, in the activated state, the molecule has been stretched, but the bond has not yet been broken.

In general, the higher the temperature required to bring about reaction, so the higher is the energy of activation. This can be seen by taking logarithms of the Arrhenius equation (4.10) and using M11.

$$\ln k = \frac{-E}{RT} + \ln A \qquad 4.14$$

It will be seen that if the rate constant (k) or $\ln k$ is to have a constant value then E/RT must also be constant. In other words if two reactions are to proceed at the same rate, E/RT for each reaction must have the same value. So E is proportional to T and the reaction requiring a high temperature is the one with a high energy of activation. In practice A does vary to some extent from reaction to reaction, so this deduction does not hold quantitatively. Nevertheless high energies of activation are associated with high reaction temperatures.

It is also worth noting that if a reaction is highly endothermic (i.e. occurs with a large absorption of heat from the surroundings) it will have a large energy of activation and will therefore require a high temperature. This follows from (4.3) where it is shown that

$$\Delta H = E_1 - E_2$$

E_1 and E_2 are the energies of activation of the forward and back reaction respectively, and ΔH is the heat of reaction.

E_1 and E_2 are necessarily positive, so that if ΔH is positive, as it is in an endothermic reaction,

$$E_1 = \Delta H + E_2$$

i.e. $$E_1 > \Delta H$$

Hence it follows that an endothermic reaction will have a large energy of activation and will therefore require a high temperature to bring about the reaction at measurable rate.

The Arrhenius equation was originally derived by using the Van't Hoff isochore (4.4) and assuming that the equilibrium constant is the ratio of the rate constants of the forward and back reactions. There is, however, an alternative way in which (4.10) can be obtained.

Arrhenius postulated that only activated molecules could bring about reaction, and hence at constant temperature it would be expected that the rate of reaction should be proportional to the fraction of molecules which were activated. Suppose that the concentration of reactants is kept constant at one gram molecule per litre. Then the rate of reaction is equal to the rate constant (k) (see page 3) and so

k is proportional to the number of activated collisions

or (using M1)

$k = A \times$ (fraction of molecules with activation energy) 4.15

where A is a proportionality constant.

From the Maxwell-Boltzmann theory of the distribution of energy among molecules it is known that the fraction of molecules possessing an energy E in addition to the average energy is equal to $\exp(-E/RT)$.

Substituting into (4.15) gives the Arrhenius equation in the exponential form (4.10), namely

$$k = A \exp \frac{-E}{RT} \qquad 4.16$$

The expression $\exp(-E/RT)$ which occurs in (4.16) is known as the Boltzmann factor. It has a very small numerical value in chemical reactions. Taking as a typical example a reaction at 25°C in which the energy of activation is 20 kcal,

$$\exp\frac{-E}{RT} = \exp\frac{(-20{,}000)}{2 \times 298} = \exp(-33{\cdot}56) = 2{\cdot}7 \times 10^{-15}$$

i.e. one collision in every $3{\cdot}7 \times 10^{14}$ will be activated as

$$3{\cdot}7 \times 10^{14} = \frac{1}{2{\cdot}7 \times 10^{-15}}$$

The population of the world is approximately two thousand million or 2×10^9. Thus the fraction of activated molecules is about one million times smaller than the fraction of the world's population who are reading this sentence at this very moment. The slow rate of chemical reactions with this activation energy can now be understood, for before reacting, the average molecule will require $3{\cdot}7 \times 10^{14}$ collisions to become activated. Even though the collision frequency is as high as 10^{11} per second per molecule, the time taken for reaction is

$$\frac{3{\cdot}7 \times 10^{14}}{10^{11}} = 3{,}700 \text{ sec or about one hour.}$$

The idea that the rate of a process is governed by an energy barrier or activation energy is one of the fundamental concepts of physical chemistry which is applied to problems outside the scope of reaction kinetics, e.g. viscosity of liquids and conductivity of semi-conductors.

If a mechanism of reaction can be found which will provide a path of lower energy of activation, there will be a corresponding increase in the rate of reaction. This is in fact how catalysts function. They provide an alternative reaction path at a low energy of activation, but are not themselves consumed in the process. Since thermodynamic properties such as free energy or heat content depend only on the initial and final state of the system, and not on the path taken, it will be expected that no correlation will exist between thermodynamic properties and reaction rates. There is none.

The Arrhenius equation is obeyed by all simple one-stage reactions. Indeed, if when the logarithm of the rate constant is plotted against the reciprocal of the absolute temperature, there is any marked deviation from a straight line, this is usually taken as an indication that the reaction is complex. The significance of the activation energy is discussed further in the next chapter on the theory of reaction rates.

THEORY OF REACTION RATES

The rate constants of many chemical reactions have been measured and the most obvious conclusion that can be drawn from the results is that, at a given temperature, the rates of various reactions may differ by many powers of ten. The theory of reaction rates explains why this should be so and attempts to predict the rate of a reaction from first principles.

There are two theoretical approaches to this problem. The first is known as the *Collision Theory of Reaction Rates*. This is based upon the idea that if two molecules are to combine chemically an essential first step is that they should meet (i.e. collide). Then, using Arrhenius's concept of an activation energy, it is postulated that not all collisions lead to reaction. Only those in which a molecule acquires more than the activation energy will be able to do so. The collision theory may therefore be expressed in a sentence by saying that the rate of reaction is equal to the number of activated collisions per unit time.

The second method of approach is based upon a more detailed consideration of the concept of a 'collision leading to reaction'. Instead of regarding the reaction of molecules as something which either happens instantaneously or does not happen, it is realized that the bond breaking and making involved in a chemical change must occur continuously and simultaneously.

Consider the reversible reaction

$$H_2 + I_2 \rightleftharpoons 2HI$$

At some stage in this reaction the H—H bond and the I—I

41

bond must be broken while H—I bonds are being formed. Thus, if a partially formed or partially broken bond is denoted by a dotted line, the reaction may be written as

$$
\begin{array}{ccc}
 & \text{H} \cdots\cdots \text{H} & \\
\text{H—H} \quad : & \quad : \quad \text{H} \quad \text{H} & \\
+ \quad \rightleftharpoons : & \quad : \rightleftharpoons | + | & \qquad 5.1 \\
\text{I—I} \quad : & \quad : \quad \text{I} \quad \text{I} & \\
 & \text{I} \cdots\cdots \text{I} &
\end{array}
$$

The intermediate product with the partially formed bonds is known at the *Transition State*. The energy required to form the transition state is the energy of activation.

The rate theory based on this model is known as the *Transition State* or *Activated Complex Theory*. It has been developed mathematically to give the *Theory of Absolute Reaction Rates* in which it is attempted to calculate the rate constant of a reaction from knowledge of the structure of the reactants.

These two approaches to the theory of reaction rates will now be described in more detail.

COLLISION THEORY OF REACTION RATES

As seen above, the essential idea of this theory is that the rate of reaction equals the number of activated collisions per unit time, i.e.

$$
\frac{dn}{dt} = Z \exp \frac{-E}{RT} \qquad 5.2
$$

where n = number of molecules of product formed at time t

Z = number of collisions per unit volume per unit time

E = energy of activation

$\exp(-E/RT)$ = fraction of collisions that are activated (see 4.16).

42

Z and dn/dt are not constants since the number of reactant molecules steadily decreases as the reaction proceeds.

Assume that equation (5.2) is applied to the second order reaction

$$A + B \rightarrow AB$$

then, by definition of the second order rate constant, k,

$$\frac{dn}{dt} = kn_A n_B \qquad 5.3$$

where n_A and n_B are the number of molecules per unit volume of A and B respectively, and k is expressed in the appropriate units.

Combining (5.2) and (5.3)

$$k = \frac{Z}{n_A n_B} \exp \frac{-E}{RT}$$

or

$$\boxed{k = Z° \exp \frac{-E}{RT}} \qquad 5.4$$

where

$$Z° = \frac{Z}{n_A n_B} \qquad 5.5$$

and is called the *Collision Number*. Equation (5.4) is a mathematical statement of the Collision Theory of Reaction Rates. It should be noted that the exponential form of the Arrhenius equation (4.10) is identical with (5.4) if the constant A is replaced by $Z°$.

From the kinetic theory of gases, the collision number is proportional to the square root of the absolute temperature, and so there are two temperature-dependent terms in the expression for k in (5.4). However, the increase in $Z°$ with temperature is so small compared with the change in the exponential term that it is usually ignored.

For example, at 27°C (300°K) a 10°C rise in temperature will increase $Z°$ by a factor of $(310/300)^{\frac{1}{2}} = 1.016$. This may be compared with a two- to three-fold increase in the exponential term for the same temperature rise.

The slight dependence of $Z°$ on temperature is not sufficient to upset the linearity of the Arrhenius plot of $\ln k$ against $1/T$ but it must be allowed for in accurate measurements of the energy of activation.

Verification of the collison theory consists of calculating the collision number $(Z°)$ and measuring the energy of activation (E) for the particular reaction. These values are substituted in the expression $Z°$ exp $(-E/RT)$ and the result compared with the experimental value of the rate constant (k).

Calculation of the collision number

From the kinetic theory of gases it is known that, in a mixture of gases A and B, the number of collisions (Z) involving one molecule of A and one molecule of B taking place in one cubic centimetre in one second is

$$Z = n_A n_B \sigma_{AB}^2 \, [8\pi RT(M_A + M_B)/M_A M_B]^{\frac{1}{2}} \qquad 5.6$$

where n_A, n_B, R and T are defined above
M_A and M_B are the molecular weights of A and B respectively. σ_{AB} is the mean collision diameter of A and B.
The collision diameter of a single molecule is the diameter of the effective target area that it presents to other colliding molecules, assuming that the molecules are spherical. The mean collision diameter of A and B is the average of their individual collision diameters, i.e.

$$\sigma_{AB} = \tfrac{1}{2}(\sigma_A + \sigma_B)$$

Now, the collision number $Z° = \dfrac{Z}{n_A n_B}$ (from 5.5)

Substitution of (5.5) into (5.6) gives

$$Z° = \sigma_{AB}^2 \, [8\pi RT(M_A + M_B)/M_A M_B]^{\frac{1}{2}} \qquad 5.7$$

The physical significance of $Z°$ is that it represents the

44

number of collisions per unit volume per unit time when the reactants are at unit concentration. This may be seen by substituting $n_A = n_B = 1$ into (5.5) giving $Z = Z°$.

In the simple case where the two reacting molecules are identical (e.g. $2HI \rightarrow H_2 + I_2$), (5.7) reduces to

$$Z° = 2\sigma^2[\pi RT/M]^{\frac{1}{2}}$$ 5.8

In deriving (5.8), equation (5.7) has been divided by two because in (5.7) the number of collisions is equal to the number of molecules of A or B that collide, whereas in (5.8), where the two molecules are identical, the number of collisions is half the number of molecules entering into collision.

Before substituting $Z°$ into (5.4) it must be converted into the appropriate units. $Z°$ has the dimensions of cc molecule^{-1} sec^{-1}, whereas the second order rate constant (k) in (5.4) has the dimensions of litre mole^{-1} sec^{-1}. Therefore $Z°$ must be multiplied by $N/1000$ (where N is the Avogadro number) before the value calculated from (5.7) is substituted into (5.4). When (5.8) is to be used the factor becomes $2N/1000$ because each collision involves two molecules of reactant.

Calculation of the collision diameter requires measurement of the viscosity of the gas, and use of the result obtained by the kinetic theory of gases that

$$\sigma^2 = \frac{2\rho}{3\pi\eta n}\left[\frac{RT}{\pi M}\right]^{\frac{1}{2}}$$ 5.9

where

σ = mean collision diameter
η = viscosity of the gas
ρ = density of the gas
n = number of molecules per cc

The collision diameter of most gas molecules is in the range of one to ten Angstrom units (Å) where $1Å = 10^{-8}$ cm. Some values of collision diameters from viscosity measurements are shown in TABLE 3.

TABLE 3.

Gas	Collision diameter (Å)	Gas	Collision diameter (Å)
hydrogen	2·5	chlorine	4·5
helium	2·2	hydrogen iodide	3·5
hydrogen chloride	2·9	carbon dioxide	4·2
nitrogen	3·5	mercury	6·3
oxygen	3·4	benzene	7·5

It should be noted that (5.9) is derived by assuming that the molecules are spherical. This is certainly not the case for HCl, HI, CO_2 and others, and so the collision diameters in these cases must be regarded as mean values.

Measurement of the Energy of Activation

All that is required here is to know the ratio of the rate constants at two temperatures, or relative values at a series of temperatures (see M16). Then by applying the Arrhenius equation the energy of activation may be found.

It is sometimes objected that in calculating the energy of activation a measurement of rate constant is used and hence it is not legitimate to use this result in the collision theory to calculate back the required theoretical rate constant. The answer to this objection is that only relative values of the rate constants at various temperatures are needed to calculate E, and these can be obtained without any knowledge of their absolute values.

Calculation of rate constant

Having calculated $Z°$ from (5.6) or (5.8) and E from (4.13), these values can be substituted into equation (5.4) to give the theoretical value of the rate constant. This may then be compared with the experimental result.

It is found in practice that (5.4) does in fact predict the rate constant of a few simple reactions. This will be illustrated with reference to the reaction.

$$2HI \rightarrow H_2 + I_2 \text{ at } 283°C$$

From the variation of rate of reaction with temperature, the energy of activation is found to be 44·0 kcal.

The collision diameter of hydrogen iodide calculated from (5.9) is 3·5Å.

At 556°K (= 283°C)

$$\exp \frac{-E}{RT} = \exp \frac{-44,000}{1·987 \times 556} = 5·08 \times 10^{-18}$$

$$Z° \text{ (litre mole}^{-1} \text{ sec}^{-1}) = \left[\frac{2N}{1000}\right]\left[2\sigma^2\left(\frac{\pi RT}{M}\right)^{\frac{1}{2}}\right] \text{ from (5.8)}$$

In this formula, σ is in cm and R is in ergs. Since 1 cal = 4·184 × 10⁷ ergs,

$$Z° = \frac{2 \times 6·02 \times 10^{23}}{1000} \times 2(3·5 \times 10^{-8})^2 \times$$

$$\left[\frac{3·142 \times 1·987 \times 4·184 \times 10^7 \times 556}{127·9}\right]^{\frac{1}{2}}$$

i.e. $Z° = 9·94 \times 10^{10}$

Hence from (5.4)

$$k = Z° \exp \frac{-E}{RT} = 5·08 \times 10^{-18} \times 9·94 \times 10^{10}$$

i.e. $k = 5·05 \times 10^{-7}$ litre mole^{-1} sec^{-1}

The experimental value of the second order rate constant at this temperature is $3·5 \times 10^{-7}$ litre mole^{-1} sec^{-1} which is in good agreement with the predicted result.

Extension of collision theory to reactions in solution

The collision number in gas reactions has been calculated in (5.7) from the kinetic theory of gases by assuming that the frequency of collision is that of incompressible spherical molecules which exert no forces on one another and are not influenced by the presence of other molecules. It therefore seems possible that in ideal solutions the frequency of collisions should approximate to that calculated by the gas method.

This approximation is justified by the fact that some reactions occur at the same rate in solution as in the gas phase, examples being the decomposition of nitrogen pentoxide and the reaction of chlorine with ozone. Supporting evidence is also found from the fact that reactions in solution often have a frequency factor close to that calculated by the collision theory.

Examples are shown in TABLE 4 below.

TABLE 4

Reactants	Solvent	E kcal	Observed log A	Calculated log A
$C_2H_5ONa + CH_3I$	ethanol	19·49	11·38	11·28
$C_2H_5Br + OH^-$	ethanol	21·40	11·63	11·57
$(CH_3)_2SO_4 + KCNS$	methanol	17·88	10·76	11·28

There are many reactions in solution, particularly between an ion and a polar molecule, where log A is between 11 and 12 (the value to be expected from collision theory).

Failure of the collision theory

Although the collision theory can account for the rate of some simple reactions, cases are known where the rates differ by many powers of ten from the values predicted by equation (5.4). For this reason the equation is often written

$$k = PZ° \exp \frac{-E}{RT} \qquad 5.10$$

where P (called the *probability* or *steric* factor) is a correcting term, which can be regarded as the ratio of the observed rate constant to that calculated from the collision theory.

48

The reaction between triethylamine and ethyl iodide in the vapour phase occurs more slowly than expected ($P = 10^{-8}$) whereas the acid hydrolysis of some sugars occurs faster than expected with values of P up to 10^{+9}. Clearly the collision theory has broken down in these cases.

Some of the reasons for the failure of the simple collision theory are as follows:

(a) It is often necessary that the reacting molecules should have a definite orientation, as well as the activation energy, before they can react. This applies particularly to large molecules. Thus consider the reaction

$$NO_2 \langle\!\!\!\!=\!\!\!\!\rangle Br + OH^- \xrightarrow[\text{ethanol}]{\text{aqueous}} Br^- + NO_2 \langle\!\!\!\!=\!\!\!\!\rangle OH$$

The hydroxyl ion must approach the carbon atom substituted by bromine if reaction is to occur. An energetic collision with the nitro group will not cause the carbon bromine bond to weaken and break.

It is thus seen that a certain degree of molecular orientation (order) is required to form the transition state. It is because of this that the concept of entropy (the thermodynamic measure of order–disorder changes) enters into more advanced rate theory. For the moment, however, it may be concluded that the orientation effect will cause a low value of P to be observed.

(b) Reactions may occur, not in a single step, but by a chain mechanism in which a molecule of product is capable of further reaction (see Chapter 9). This will cause high P factors.

(c) The energy of activation may be distributed among several bonds in the transition state, instead of being localized in the bond that breaks in the reaction. In this case the fraction of activated molecules is greater than $\exp(-E/RT)$, leading to high P factors (see Chapter 6).

(d) If the reaction occurs on a catalytic surface the collision theory cannot be applied since the rate of reaction does not depend on the number of collisions in the gas (see Chapter 8).

Summing up, the collision theory gives a satisfactory account of the rates of a few of the simplest reactions, but needs major modifications if it is to be generally applicable.

TRANSITION STATE THEORY

The main assumption of this theory is that all chemical reactions proceed via a transition state which is in thermodynamic equilibrium with the reactants even though the overall chemical reaction is irreversible. This may be symbolized as

$$A + B \rightleftharpoons C^{\ddagger} \rightarrow \text{Products.}$$

where the superscript $\ddagger$ refers to the transition state.

The rate of reaction is assumed to be proportional to the concentration of the activated molecules ($c^{\ddagger}$) and this concentration is governed by the laws of chemical equilibria. Thus if $K^{\ddagger}$ refers to the equilibrium constant for formation of the transition state, and a, b and $c^{\ddagger}$ represent the concentrations of A, B and $C^{\ddagger}$ at time t, then

$$K^{\ddagger} = c^{\ddagger}/ab \text{ or } c^{\ddagger} = K^{\ddagger}ab \qquad 5.11$$

The rate of reaction is proportional to the concentration of the transition state ($c^{\ddagger}$), or

$$\frac{dx}{dt} = mc^{\ddagger} \qquad 5.12$$

where m is a proportionality constant.

But, by the definition of a second order rate constant (k), see (1.8).

$$\frac{dx}{dt} = kab \qquad 5.13$$

Equating (5.12) with (5.13)

$$k = \frac{mc^{\ddagger}}{ab} = mK^{\ddagger} \text{ (from 5.11)} \qquad 5.14$$

By considering the equilibrium from the viewpoint of

statistical and quantum mechanics it has been shown that the constant m is equal to RT/Nh.

where
$$N = \text{Avogadro number}$$
$$h = \text{Planck's constant}$$

Thus (5.14) becomes

$$k = \frac{RTK^{\ddagger}}{Nh} \qquad 5.15$$

This factor RT/Nh is the same for all molecules irrespective of their chemical properties. This equation is not directly useful since $K^{\ddagger}$ cannot be measured experimentally. However, assuming that the transition state is in true thermodynamic equilibrium with the reactants, the thermodynamic result

$$\varDelta G^{\ddagger} = \varDelta H^{\ddagger} - T\varDelta S^{\ddagger} = -RT\ln K^{\ddagger} \qquad 5.16$$

may be applied where

$\varDelta G^{\ddagger}$ = standard free energy of formation of the transition state

$\varDelta H^{\ddagger}$ = standard enthalpy (heat content) of formation of the transition state (energy of activation)

$\varDelta S^{\ddagger}$ = standard entropy of formation of transition state (entropy of activation)

From (5.16)
$$\ln K^{\ddagger} = \frac{T\varDelta S^{\ddagger} - \varDelta H^{\ddagger}}{RT} \qquad 5.17$$

Using (M9) and (M10),

$$K^{\ddagger} = \exp\left(\frac{\varDelta S^{\ddagger}}{R}\right) \exp\left(\frac{-\varDelta H^{\ddagger}}{RT}\right) \qquad 5.18$$

If this result is substituted into (5.15)

$$k = \frac{RT}{Nh} \exp\left(\frac{\varDelta S^{\ddagger}}{R}\right) \exp\left(\frac{-\varDelta H^{\ddagger}}{RT}\right) \qquad 5.19$$

Equation (5.19) is the expression for the rate constant of a reaction derived from transition state theory. It is useful to compare this with the corresponding equation from collision theory, namely

$$k = PZ° \exp \frac{-E}{RT} \qquad 5.10$$

The exponential terms involving energy in (5.10) and (5.19) are the same since $\Delta H^{\ddagger}$ represents the increase in heat content on forming the transition state from the reactants, which is the energy of activation, E.

RT/Nh is a numerical factor (proportional to temperature) which at 25°C has a numerical value of about 10^{13}, whereas $Z°$ (which is proportional to the square root of T) is roughly 10^{11} at 25°C.

The significant difference between (5.10) and (5.19) is that the term $PZ°$ of the collision theory is now replaced by $RT/Nh \exp(\Delta S^{\ddagger}/R)$, which enables deviations from the collision theory to be interpreted in terms of entropy (or order–disorder) changes in forming the transition state.

Thus if a reaction requires a specific orientation of the reactants, the transition state is more ordered than the initial state, i.e. $\Delta S^{\ddagger}$ is negative and $\exp(\Delta S^{\ddagger}/R)$ is less than one. This means that the rate of reaction predicted by the transition state theory will be less than that predicted on simple collision theory which is in fact the case. It corresponds to a value of P less than one.

Conversely, if the transition state is more disordered than the initial state $\Delta S^{\ddagger}$ will be positive, corresponding to a high value of P. This occurs in unimolecular gas reactions in which the energy of activation is distributed among several bonds in the transition state.

Quite small changes in entropy produce a large kinetic effect. For example if $\Delta S^{\ddagger} = 20$ cal mole^{-1} deg^{-1}, then

$$\frac{\Delta S^{\ddagger}}{R} = 10$$

$$\therefore \exp \frac{\Delta S^{\ddagger}}{R} = \exp(10) \simeq 2 \times 10^4.$$

Thus the value of P found by using the collision theory

would be about 10^4. An entropy change of 40 cal mole^{-1} deg^{-1} is needed to account for P factors of 10^8. This is, however, less than the entropy of a diatomic gas at s.t.p.

When reactions occur by the same mechanism in the gas phase and in solution then, provided solvation is not involved, $\Delta S^{\ddagger}$ and ΔH should be the same for both reactions. In this way it can be explained why a few reactions occur at the same rate in solution and in the gas phase.

It is now possible to give some account of the widespread variation in rate from reaction to reaction in terms of two factors, namely the energy and entropy of activation. In general the energy of activation will depend on the strength of the bonds that are broken and formed in the transition state but it will also be considerably influenced by factors such as solvation. The numerical value may vary from 10 kcals to 80 kcals. At room temperature this variation in energy of activation would give rate constants which differed by a factor of 10^{50}. The energy of activation is the major factor in determining the rate of reaction.

The entropy term ($\Delta S_{\ddagger}$) is not so easy to visualize as is the energy of activation. However, it plays a profound part in reactions in which orientation of molecules is involved. Its magnitude is sufficient in extreme cases to give rates of reaction which differ by a factor of 10^{10}.

One purpose of the theory of reaction rates is to predict the rates of chemical reactions from knowledge of molecular structure. The collision theory is of no use for this purpose as quantitative significance cannot be attached to the probability factor P. However, the transition state theory shows (5.19) that the problem of predicting rates of reaction may be reduced to one of predicting energies and entropies of activation. In the Theory of Absolute Reaction Rates an attempt is made to do this by combining the results of quantum and of statistical mechanics. This cannot be discussed here except to say that in some simple cases, such as the conversion of para-hydrogen to ortho-hydrogen by atomic hydrogen, reasonable results have been obtained

6

FIRST ORDER REACTIONS

First order reactions present a special problem in kinetic studies. As has been already mentioned, most reactions with a one-stage mechanism obey second order rate laws since the rate of reaction is proportional to the number of collisions which in turn is proportional to the product of two concentration terms. As an example, the homogeneous thermal decomposition of nitrous oxide in the gas phase

$$2N_2O \rightarrow 2N_2 + O_2$$

is a second order reaction, as expected.

There are, however, many reactions in both the gas and the liquid phase which obey first order kinetics. This poses the problem of why the reaction is not of second order. The answer must be found in the conditions or mechanism of the reaction.

Another way of realizing the difficulty raised by first order reactions is to ask the question 'what is the origin of the energy of activation?' If a reaction is strictly first order then continually decreasing the concentration will not alter its half-life (2.11). In the extreme case, an isolated molecule would still be expected to react with the same half-life as that observed at high concentrations. But it is difficult indeed to see how an isolated molecule can acquire the necessary energy of activation.

To answer these queries, several examples will be considered in which first order kinetics are observed.

1. *Radioactive decay*

These are nuclear, not chemical, reactions, their rates being determined by changes in the nucleus rather than by changes in the energy levels of the outer electrons. They do not therefore come under the heading of chemical kinetics but it is worth noting that the rates of radioactive decay obey first order laws. Temperatures of up to a few thousand degrees have no effect on the rate of nuclear decay as the activation energy comes from within the nucleus, and is, in any case, millions of times greater than the energies involved in molecular collisions.

2. *Pseudo-unimolecular reactions*

These are bimolecular reactions in which one component is present in large excess, as, for example, if the solvent is one of the reactants. Although the reaction is bimolecular, the experimental results will obey a first order law as it is impossible to detect the change brought about by the reaction in concentration of the component in excess. For example, the molarity of water is $1000/18 = 55 \cdot 6$. If an $0 \cdot 1$ molar solution of ethyl acetate is completely hydrolysed according to the equation below, the water concentration will be reduced by $0 \cdot 1$ in $55 \cdot 6$, i.e. by less than $0 \cdot 2$ per cent.

The fact that a reaction of this type is bimolecular can be shown by adding an inert solvent. Thus in reaction (b) if ethanol is replaced by a dilute solution of ethanol in benzene, the reaction rate will depend on the ethanol concentration, thus giving a second order rate law.

Two examples of pseudo-unimolecular reactions are

(a) $CH_3COOC_2H_5 + H_2O \rightarrow CH_3COOH + C_2H_5OH$

(b) $CH_3COCl + C_2H_5OH \rightarrow CH_3CO_2C_2H_5 + HCl$

3. *Reactions in solution*

If a reaction occurs in a series of steps and the rate determining step is unimolecular, then first order kinetics will be observed. This occurs in the hydrolysis of tertiary amyl iodide and is discussed in more detail in Chapter 7.

4. *First order gas reactions*

First order kinetics can result from homogeneous

heterogeneous or chain reactions in the gas phase. There are also some complex reactions, such as the decomposition of nitrogen pentoxide, which obey the first order laws. This latter case is discussed in Chapter 7, page 71 and heterogeneous and chain reactions are considered in Chapters 8 and 9 respectively. The remainder of this chapter will therefore be devoted to unimolecular gas reactions, i.e., reactions in which the activated complex is formed from a single reactant molecule.

A reaction in the gas phase is assumed to be unimolecular if it (a) obeys accurately the first order rate law, (b) is homogeneous, (c) is not a chain reaction, (d) changes order from one to two at a pressure of a few millimetres.

The absence of surface effects is shown if altering the ratio of surface area to volume (e.g. by adding powdered glass) produces no change in the rate of reaction. The absence of chain reactions is shown by the use of inhibitors (see Chapter 9).

Unimolecular gas reactions are not common, two examples being

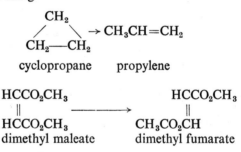

cyclopropane   propylene

dimethyl maleate   dimethyl fumarate

The problem of the origin of the energy of activation in a unimolecular gas reaction is a difficult one. It was finally solved in 1923 by F. A. Lindemann (later Lord Cherwell). He pointed out that it is possible for molecules to receive their energy of activation by collision, and still obey first order kinetics, if there is a time delay between activation and reaction during which most of the activated molecules are de-activated by collision with normal molecules. If A represents the normal molecule and A* is the activated molecule, the Lindemann mechanism may be formulated as follows:

$$A + A \overset{k_1}{\underset{k_2}{\rightleftharpoons}} A + A^* \qquad 6.1$$

$$A^* \overset{k_3}{\to} \text{products} \qquad 6.2$$

where k_1, k_2, k_3 are the rate constants in (6.1) and (6.2)

The exact solution of the kinetic equations that describe this mechanism is difficult but a simple result may be obtained using an approximation known as the *Stationary State Hypothesis*. This states that when reaction is brought about by very reactive molecules present at low concentrations, the concentration of such molecules may be regarded as constant.

If only a small fraction of the activated molecules (A*) react to give product (the majority being de-activated), a stationary concentration of A* will be built up so that the rate of formation of A* equals the rate of its removal. Under these circumstances the concentration of A*, and hence the rate of reaction, will be proportional to the concentration of A. The reaction will therefore be first order. This argument can be seen mathematically by referring to the Lindemann mechanism shown in (6.1) and (6.2).

Rate of formation of A* = rate of destruction of A*   6.3

If a and a^* represent the concentrations of A and A* at time t the stationary state hypothesis may be expressed mathematically by the equation

$$\frac{\mathrm{d}a^*}{\mathrm{d}t} = 0 \qquad 6.4$$

which is equivalent to (6.3).

From (6.1) rate of formation of $A^* = k_1a^2$

From (6.1) and (6.2)

rate of destruction of $A^* = k_2a^*a + k_3a^*$

Using (6.3) $\qquad k_1a^2 = k_2a^*a + k_3a^*$

Re-arranging

$$a^* = \frac{k_1a^2}{k_2a + k_3} \qquad 6.5$$

From (6.2) the rate of formation of product is k_3a^* and hence the rate of reaction ($-\mathrm{d}a/\mathrm{d}t$) will be given by

$$\boxed{\frac{-\mathrm{d}a}{\mathrm{d}t} = \frac{k_1k_3a^2}{k_2a + k_3}} \qquad 6.6$$

At high pressures k_2a is much greater than k_3 (i.e. more molecules are de-activated than react). Hence k_3 can be ignored in comparison with k_2a and so (6.6) becomes

$$\frac{-\mathrm{d}a}{\mathrm{d}t} = \frac{k_1k_3a}{k_2} = ka \qquad 6.7$$

Since k_1k_3/k_2 is itself a constant (k), (6.7) is a first order law.

The above argument is based on the assumption that many more molecules of A^* are de-activated than react to give product. If the pressure of the gas is continuously reduced, the time between collisions increases, until it eventually becomes greater than the time interval between activation and reaction. As a result, the fraction of activated molecules that react gradually increases, until, at very low pressures, all the activated molecules react. When this happens the rate of reaction is proportional to the rate of formation of A^* i.e. to k_1a^2. At low pressures the reaction will therefore be of second order. This may be seen directly from (6.6). When a is sufficiently small k_2a becomes smaller than k_3 when (6.6) becomes

$$\frac{-\mathrm{d}a}{\mathrm{d}t} = k_1a^2$$

which is a second order equation.

Thus, below a certain pressure, usually 5 to 50 mm of mercury, the order of the reaction should change gradually from one to two. This effect is in fact observed with unimolecular reactions.

The Lindemann mechanism has been confirmed by the effect of added hydrogen. If a unimolecular gas reaction is carried out in the presence of hydrogen at a partial pressure that would correspond to a second order reaction in the pure gas, it is found that the reaction is first order with the same rate constant as observed in the high pressure gas reaction. This is to be expected from the fact that the essential feature of this mechanism is that the activated molecules can be de-activated by collision during the time delay between activation and reaction. This is not a chemical process and can be brought about by any molecule that collides with the activated molecule A^*. In the presence of hydrogen, the de-activating reaction

$$A^* + H_2 \rightarrow A + H_2$$

occurs rapidly compared with the conversion of A^* to products, thus maintaining the basic requirements of the Lindemann mechanism.

It is surprising that other inert gases such as helium, nitrogen and carbon dioxide do not have the de-activating effect shown by hydrogen, which is remarkably efficient in removing energy from activated molecules.

Supporting evidence in favour of a delay between activation and reaction comes from the phenomenon known as 'pre-dissociation' observed in molecular spectroscopy. In these spectra the vibrational bands for the activated molecules are present but the fine structure due to the rotation of the molecule is absent. The explanation given of this effect is that the activated molecule exists for only a short time (10^{-12} sec) after which it reacts chemically. This time is long enough for many vibrations to occur, but is not long enough for the relatively slow process of rotation, and so there is no rotational fine structure.

The application of the collision theory of reaction rates to unimolecular reactions leads to a surprising result. If the majority of the molecules are de-activated before they react it would be expected that the P factor in equation (5.10) $[k = PZ° \exp(-E/RT)]$ should be much less than one. In practice it usually has a value of 10^3 to 10^4.

The reason for this is that the Boltzmann factor, $\exp(-E/RT)$, used to calculated the fraction of activated molecules (see 4.16) does not allow for the internal degrees of vibration in a molecule. It can be shown that if the energy of activation (E) is distributed among several vibrational degrees of freedom, the fraction of molecules having the activation energy is

$$\frac{(E/RT)^{s-1}}{(s-1)!} \exp \frac{-E}{RT} \qquad 6.8$$

Where $s =$ number of vibrational degrees of freedom.

If $s = 1$, (6.8) reduces to $\qquad \dfrac{(E/RT)^0}{O!} \exp \dfrac{-E}{RT}$

Using M6 and M7, $x^0 = O! = 1$

i.e. (6.8) reduces to the normal form for the Boltzmann factor, namely $\exp(-E/RT)$.

The expression (6.8) becomes considerably larger than $\exp(-E/RT)$ when s is greater than 1. Thus if $E = 20,000$ cal and $s = 8$ then at 25°C

$$\frac{(E/RT)^{s-1}}{(s-1)!} = \frac{1}{7!}\left(\frac{20,000}{1·987 \times 298}\right)^7 = 9·96 \times 10^6$$

Unimolecular reactions are those in which there is a delay between activation and reaction. The classical theory, due to Kassel and Hinshelwood, accounts for this by assuming that the energy of activation is distributed among several bonds in the activated molecule and that the delay is due to the time required to transfer the energy to the bond involved in the reaction. This means usually that the molecules are complex ones with many bonds and so s is large. The corrected Boltzmann factor (6.8) more than compensates for the molecules de-activated by collision and so accounts for the high P factor observed experimentally.

For several years the decomposition of nitrogen pentoxide was the only known case of a first order gas reaction, which was homogeneous and not a chain reaction. It does not fit in to the Lindemann mechanism since it remains first order down to a pressure of 0·05 mm mercury. This decomposition is discussed as a special case in Chapter 7.

7

DETERMINATION OF MECHANISM BY KINETIC METHODS

The kinetic method is a valuable tool in the investigation of reaction mechanisms. This is particularly so where the mechanism involves two or more successive reactions, for by kinetic measurements information can be obtained about the number of molecules involved in the slowest, or rate-determining, step. This information cannot usually be obtained by other methods.

To illustrate the applications of the kinetic method, six examples have been chosen in which kinetic studies have played a vital part in determining mechanism.

1. *The reaction of acetone with iodine*

This reaction was studied by Lapworth in 1904 and was one of the first mechanisms to be studied kinetically. If a dilute solution of iodine in acidic aqueous acetone is allowed to stand at room temperature a slow reaction occurs represented by the equation

$$CH_3COCH_3 + I_2 \xrightarrow{\text{acid}} CH_3COCH_2I + HI$$

It may be followed by removing aliquots, adding excess of potassium iodide solution and titrating the iodine remaining with sodium thiosulphate solution. If the concentration of the acid catalyst is considerably greater than that of the iodine solution the reaction is of zero order, i.e. the rate of reaction is constant with time and does not depend upon the concentration of iodine or acetone. FIGURE 6 shows the typical results obtained from four experiments (a), (b), (c), (d). The corresponding initial concentrations of iodine increase steadily from experiment (a) to experiment (d).

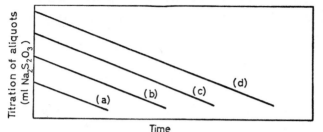

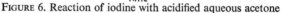

FIGURE 6. Reaction of iodine with acidified aqueous acetone

Of the four chemical species present, acetone, water and the acid catalyst are present in excess, and so their concentrations would not be expected to occur in the rate law. It is, however, most surprising that the rate of reaction does not depend on the concentration of the iodine.

The basic theoretical principle used in interpreting this fact is that the kinetic results describe what is happening in the rate-determining step of the reaction. Hence the logical conclusion is that the rate-determining step does not involve iodine.

Having established this, it is now necessary to postulate a mechanism which is consistent with general chemical knowledge and with the observed kinetics. It is well known that some ketones (e.g. ethyl acetoacetate) undergo a slow reversible change from a keto to an enol form. If this type of equilibrium is set up in acetone the mechanism can be explained as

$$CH_3COCH_3 \overset{acid}{\rightleftharpoons} CH_3 \cdot \underset{\underset{OH}{|}}{C}=CH_2 \qquad \text{Slow} \qquad 7.1$$

$$CH_3 \cdot \underset{\underset{OH}{|}}{C}=CH_2 + I_2 \rightarrow CH_3 - \underset{\underset{OH}{|}}{CI} - CH_2I \qquad \text{Fast} \qquad 7.2$$

$$CH_3 - \underset{\underset{OH}{|}}{CI} \cdot CH_2I \rightarrow HI + CH_3COCH_2I \qquad \text{Fast} \qquad 7.3$$

63

In this mechanism the rate-determining step (7.1) does not involve iodine, in agreement with experiment. Also it may be predicted that the rate of bromination of acetone, and the rate of deuterium exchange should be both equal to the rate of iodination, as both involve reaction with the double bond in the enol form. This has been verified experimentally.

Examination of (7.3) shows that acid is produced in the reaction. Hence the zero order law will only be obeyed if the initial concentration of acid catalyst is relatively large, so that the concentration during the reaction remains effectively constant.

If the reaction is carried out with a small initial amount of acid catalyst the phenomenon of *autocatalysis* is observed. This is shown in FIGURE 7. The essential feature is that initially the rate of reaction increases with time as more acid is produced. By measuring the rate of the autocatalytic reaction in different proportions of acetone to water it has been shown that

$$\text{rate} \propto [\text{acetone}] [\text{acid}]$$

It may therefore be concluded that the observed zero order reaction is bimolecular, as one molecule of acid and one molecule of acetone are involved in the rate-determining step.

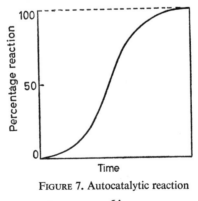

FIGURE 7. Autocatalytic reaction

This result implies that (7.1) is not a simple one stage process. It must involve addition of the acid catalyst, followed at some stage by its elimination, since the acid is not consumed in the overall reaction.

2. *Nitration of aromatic hydrocarbons*

The kinetics of nitration are too complex to discuss as a whole, but one point of interest will be mentioned.

Benford and Ingold showed in 1938 that if nitration of aromatic hydrocarbons is carried out in organic solvents such as glacial acetic acid, and if an excess of nitric acid is used and the hydrocarbon is a reactive one, then the reaction is of zero order. Thus the same rate of nitration is measured for benzene, toluene and ethyl benzene in glacial acetic acid and in all three cases the rate is independent of the concentration of the hydrocarbon. (The corresponding reactions in a mixture of nitric and sulphuric acids are too fast to measure).

Since the nitric acid is present in excess, its concentration would not be expected in the rate law. It is, however, surprising that the rate should be independent of the concentration of the hydrocarbon. The explanation of this fact is that the hydrocarbon cannot be involved in the rate-determining step of the reaction. It is therefore concluded that the slow step in the reaction is the conversion of nitric acid into the nitrating agent.

By combining spectroscopic, cryoscopic and kinetic evidence it was deduced that nitration is brought about by the nitronium ion (NO_2^+) which is formed slowly from nitric acid according to the equation

$$2HNO_3 \rightleftharpoons NO_2^+ + NO_3^- + H_2O \qquad 7.4$$

If the aromatic hydrocarbon has a high reactivity it removes nitronium ions as fast as they are formed, and the rate of reaction is determined by the reaction (7.4). The rate is therefore independent of the hydrocarbon concentration.

3. *The reaction of hydrogen peroxide with hydriodic acid*

Hydrogen peroxide and hydriodic acid react in dilute aqueous solution at room temperature to form iodine according to the equation

$$H_2O_2 + 2HI \rightarrow 2H_2O + I_2 \qquad 7.5$$

The reaction is rather too quick to follow by removing aliquots and so an indirect technique is used. A small known excess of sodium thiosulphate solution and starch indicator is added to the acidified reaction mixture and the time for the formation of the blue colour is noted. Further thiosulphate is immediately added and the time for the reappearance of the blue starch colour again noted. This is repeated several times.

Iodine reacts rapidly and irreversibly with sodium thiosulphate according to the equation

$$I_2 + 2Na_2S_2O_3 \rightarrow 2NaI + Na_2S_4O_6 \qquad 7.6$$

The blue starch colour is not formed until the sodium thiosulphate has been consumed, and so the reaction mixture titrates itself. The amount of hydrogen peroxide consumed at the time when the blue colour forms is equivalent to the volume of thiosulphate added.

An important kinetic consequence of (7.6) is that the concentration of iodide ions remains constant, for any iodine formed is immediately converted back to iodide by the thiosulphate. The observed kinetics will therefore depend only on the hydrogen peroxide concentration, and experimentally the reaction is found to obey a first order rate law as would be expected. On repeating the experiment with a different initial concentration of hydriodic acid, a first order constant is again obtained, but it has a different numerical value. By carrying out several kinetic measurements it is found that the first order rate constant is directly proportional to the initial concentration of hydriodic acid. Hence

$$\text{rate} \propto [HI]\,[H_2O_2] \qquad 7.7$$

The reaction is therefore first order, and is bimolecular.

The kinetic implications of equation (7.7) are that one molecule of HI and one molecule of H_2O_2 are involved in the rate-determining step of the reaction. Since the mechanism of the reaction must also allow for the overall stoichiometry, the reaction probably proceeds as follows

$$H_2O_2 + HI \rightarrow HIO + H_2O \text{ slow}$$

followed by $HIO + HI \rightarrow H_2O + I_2$ fast

by addition, $H_2O_2 + 2HI \rightarrow 2H_2O + I_2$

which is the overall chemical reaction (see 7.5). The rate of this reaction is increased by the addition of mineral acids, and an alternative mechanism involving hydrogen ions becomes important in such solutions.

4. *The oxidation of nitric oxide*

This reaction obeys the equation

$$2NO + O_2 \rightarrow 2NO_2$$

and since it involves a decrease in number of molecules, it may be followed manometrically by measuring the decrease in pressure at constant volume. It is found experimentally that the reaction obeys the third order law

$$\frac{-d[NO]}{dt} = k[NO]^2[O_2] \qquad 7.8$$

A surprising feature of the reaction is that it has an apparently negative energy of activation, that is, that the rate of reaction decreases as the temperature increases.

Third order reactions are uncommon. Theoretically, it can be shown that the probability of a three body activated collision occurring is very small compared to the probability of an activated two body collision. Hence the mechanism is unlikely to be termolecular.

The nitric oxide molecule (like nitrogen dioxide, NO_2) is unusual in that it contains an odd number of electrons. It is well known that nitrogen dioxide tends to dimerize according to the equation

$$2NO_2 \rightleftharpoons N_2O_4 \qquad 7.9$$

Furthermore, the N_2O_4 is thermally unstable and as the temperature is increased the equilibrium is driven from right to left.

The kinetic results for the oxidation of nitric oxide can be explained if it is assumed that an equilibrium similar to (7.9) is set up, i.e.

$$2NO \rightleftharpoons N_2O_2 \qquad 7.10$$

followed by $\qquad N_2O_2 + O_2 \rightarrow 2NO_2$

Only the N_2O_2 molecules react with oxygen.
If K is the equilibrium constant for (7.10)

$$K = \frac{[N_2O_2]}{[NO]^2}$$

i.e. $\qquad [N_2O_2] = k[NO]^2 \qquad 7.11$

Assuming a second order reaction between N_2O_2 and O_2, its rate is proportional to $[N_2O_2][O_2]$
Hence, using (7.11)

$$\frac{-d[NO]}{dt} = k[NO]^2[O_2]$$

which is in agreement with the experimental result for the rate law (7.8). There is some direct experimental evidence for (7.10) since N_2O_2 has been isolated at low temperatures. Also, at room temperature there are some bands in the ultraviolet spectrum of nitric oxide whose intensity is proportional to the square of the pressure. Equation (7.11) shows that these could be attributed to N_2O_2.

An explanation of the negative energy of activation of the reaction is that the equilibrium (7.10) is affected by temperature in the same way as is (7.9). Although raising the temperature increases the rate constant for the reaction of N_2O_2 with oxygen, this is more than offset by the decrease in the concentration of N_2O_2 brought about by thermal decomposition.

One final piece of evidence in favour of this mechanism is that the reactions of nitric oxide with hydrogen, chlorine and bromine respectively are all third order, and can be explained in terms of an intermediate N_2O_2. The only examples of third order gas reactions are those involving nitric oxide.

5. *Nucleophilic substitution of alkyl halides*

Alkyl halides (RX) will, in certain cases, react with hydroxyl ions in aqueous ethanol in such a way that the halide (X) is replaced by the hydroxyl group.

$$RX + OH^- \rightarrow ROH + X^- \qquad 7.12$$

This substitution reaction is classified as nucleophilic since the reagent (in this case OH^-) is one that will attack a positive centre (i.e. a region of low electron density).

There are two distinct mechanisms by which a nucleophilic substitution reaction, such as (7.12), can occur. These are

(a) a one-step bimolecular process

$$RX + OH^- \rightarrow ROH + X^- \qquad 7.13$$

(b) a two-step process, involving a unimolecular ionisation

$$RX \rightarrow R^+ + X^- \qquad \text{slow}$$
$$\qquad\qquad\qquad\qquad\qquad 7.14$$
$$R^+ + OH^- \rightarrow ROH \qquad \text{fast}$$

Reactions of both types have been extensively studied by Hughes and Ingold who use the terms S_N2 and S_N1 to represent the mechanisms in (7.13) and (7.14) respectively. The term S_N1 is a convenient abbreviation for a unimolecular nucleophilic substitution, similarly S_N2 refers to bimolecular nucleophilic substitution.

Kinetically, it is expected that the S_N1 reaction will have an order of one. But the S_N2 reaction will have an order of two, unless one of the reactants is present in excess when the reaction will be pseudo-unimolecular (see page 55) and of order one.

The reaction of straight-chain primary alkyl halides with hydroxyl ions in aqueous ethanol obeys the second order rate law and is an S_N2 process. With tertiary alkyl halides, however, the strength of the carbon-halogen bond is weakened and ionization is easier. This is because the electron releasing effect of a tertiary group is greater than that of a straight chain. Thus in the tertiary halides, the carbon-halogen bond is polarized in the direction that facilitates ionization.

In the reactions of tertiary amyl and butyl iodides with dilute sodium hydroxide solution the reactions are found to be first order and the rate is independent of the concentration of hydroxide ions. The possibility of a pseudo-unimolecular reaction with the solvent is ruled out, since the hydroxyl ion is a much more powerful base than the solvent, and if it does not react directly with the halide, it is unlikely that the solvent will. The kinetics therefore suggest an S_N1 mechanism for this reaction.

A kinetically interesting reaction is the hydrolysis of secondary butyl bisulphate by hydroxide ions in aqueous solution,

$$RSO_4^- + OH^- \rightarrow ROH + SO_4^{2-} \qquad 7.15$$

where R is the group $(CH_3CH_2CH \cdot CH_3)$.

This is a first order reaction, the rate being independent of the concentration of hydroxide ions. This suggests that the mechanism should be S_N1. However, by using optically active *sec*-butyl bisulphate, and measuring the initial and final optical rotation, it was found that the resultant *sec*-butanol had suffered an inversion of configuration (Walden Inversion) but was still optically active. On the S_N1 mechanism an alkyl cation (R^+) having a planar structure is postulated. When the hydroxyl ion attacks the planar

70

structure (R^+) equal quantities of dextro- and laevo-forms are produced and the sample should lose its optical activity. This is contrary to the observed facts.

Examination of the reaction in question (7.15) shows that the two reactants are both negatively charged ions, which will tend to repel each other electrostatically. As a result, the uncharged water molecule is a more powerful reagent than the hydroxide ion in this particular case and the reaction occurs according to the equations

$$RSO_4^- + H_2O \rightarrow ROH + HSO_4^- \qquad \text{slow}$$

$$HSO_4^- + OH^- \rightarrow H_2O + SO_4^{2-} \qquad \text{fast}$$

The reaction is therefore S_N2 but since the water is present in large excess, the kinetics will obey a first order (pseudo-unimolecular) law. The S_N2 mechanism will explain the optical activity results stated above.

The distinction between S_N1 and S_N2 reactions is of great importance in organic chemistry, where it has been applied to evaluate the effect of substituents on substitution reactions.

6. *The thermal decomposition of nitrogen pentoxide*

This reaction is of historical importance as it was the first example to be discovered of a homogeneous first order gas reaction (1921). The reaction can be conveniently followed manometrically since it is accompanied by an increase in pressure at constant volume.

$$2N_2O_5 \rightarrow 4NO_2 + O_2 \qquad 7.16$$

Careful examination has shown that the rate is not changed by surface effects and that the reaction is uncatalysed. But it has one surprising feature. According to the Lindemann theory of unimolecular gas reactions (Chapter 6) the order should change from one to two as the pressure is lowered. Further, the critical pressure at which the kinetic order

changes can be calculated and it should be several millimetres of mercury. However, the decomposition of nitrogen
pentoxide accurately obeys the first order law down to a
pressure of 0·05 mm of mercury, and eventually becomes
second order at 0·004 mm. It is impossible to account
quantitatively for these pressure limits in terms of a simple
unimolecular decomposition.

Ogg (1947) proposed the following mechanism which is
consistent with the known experimental facts.

$$N_2O_5 \underset{k_2}{\overset{k_1}{\rightleftharpoons}} NO_2 + NO_3 \qquad \text{fast} \qquad 7.17$$

$$NO_2 + NO_3 \overset{k_3}{\rightarrow} NO_2 + O_2 + NO \quad \text{slow} \qquad 7.18$$

$$NO + NO_3 \rightarrow 2NO_2 \qquad \text{fast} \qquad 7.19$$

The NO_3 molecule is not one of the stable oxides of
nitrogen. It has not been isolated in the pure state, but its
existence has been claimed in the products of a glow
discharge of a mixture of nitrogen tetroxide and oxygen.
It was postulated in Ogg's mechanism in order to explain
the kinetic results.

This mechanism will give rise to first order kinetics in
which the observed first order rate constant (k) is given by

$$k = \frac{2k_1k_3}{k_2 + 2k_3} \qquad 7.20$$

This may be shown by applying the stationary state
hypothesis (see Chapter 6, page 57) to the unstable intermediate NO_3.

Let the concentration of N_2O_5 at time $t = a$
Let the concentration of NO_2 at time $t = b$
Let the concentration of NO_3 at time $t = c$
Using (7.17) to (7.19)

$$\frac{dc}{dt} = k_1a - k_2bc - 2k_3bc = 0 \qquad 7.21$$

The factor of 2 is used because for each NO_3 destroyed in

(7.18) one NO molecule is formed which rapidly destroys NO_3 by reaction (7.19).

From (7.21)

$$bc = \frac{k_1 a}{(k_2 + 2k_3)} \qquad 7.22$$

Since (7.17) is a rapid and reversible equilibrium, it causes no change in the concentration of nitrogen pentoxide.

The rate of reaction is therefore governed by (7.18) and hence

$$\frac{-\mathrm{d}a}{\mathrm{d}t} = 2k_3 bc. \qquad 7.23$$

Substituting (7.23) in (7.22)

$$\frac{-\mathrm{d}a}{\mathrm{d}t} = \frac{2k_1 k_3 a}{k_2 + 2k_3} \qquad 7.24$$

Remembering that a represents the concentration of nitrogen pentoxide, equation (7.24) states that the rate of reaction of nitrogen pentoxide is proportional to its concentration, the proportionality constant (i.e. the rate constant) being $2k_1 k_3/(k_2 + 2k_3)$ in agreement with the stated value in (7.20), giving a satisfactory account of the first order kinetics.

The postulated mechanism has been verified in the following ways:

(a) If (7.17) is a rapid and reversible reaction, there should be isotope exchange between nitrogen pentoxide and nitrogen dioxide enriched in the isotope ^{15}N

$$N_2O_5 + {}^{15}NO_2 \rightleftharpoons NO_2 + NO_3 + {}^{15}NO_2 \rightleftharpoons {}^{15}N_2O_5 + NO_2 \qquad 7.25$$

This exchange has been demonstrated experimentally. Furthermore, the rate of isotope exchange is a measure of the rate of the unimolecular decomposition of N_2O_5 shown in (7.17). The value of k_1 obtained by this method is much greater than k (the observed first order rate constant for the whole process) which is in agreement with the postulate that (7.18) is the rate determining step.

By measuring the rate of isotope exchange at various pressures it is possible to show that the rate of the unimolecular stage of the reaction (7.17) varies with pressure in accordance with the Lindemann theory. In fact k_1 begins to change from first to second order at a pressure of 50 mm of mercury.

(b) The rate of the reaction of nitric oxide with nitrogen pentoxide has been measured

$$NO + N_2O_5 \rightarrow 3NO_2 \qquad 7.26$$

and is independent of the concentration of nitric oxide. If, however, a reversible equilibrium (7.17) is set up the mechanism of (7.26) could be explained as follows:

$$N_2O_5 \rightleftharpoons NO_2 + NO_3 \qquad \text{slow}$$

$$NO + NO_3 \rightarrow 2NO_2 \qquad \text{fast} \qquad 7.27$$

It must be remembered that 'fast' and 'slow' are relative terms, so that although (7.17) is fast compared to (7.18) it is slow compared to (7.27).

This experiment is evidence for the existence of the equilibrium postulated in (7.17).

8

HETEROGENEOUS REACTIONS AND CATALYSIS

In many chemical reactions, including some of industrial importance, reaction occurs on a solid surface and not uniformly throughout the gas or liquid surrounding the solid. Such reactions are heterogeneous.

When the surface is involved in the reaction mechanism, the rate of reaction at a given temperature depends mainly upon the area of the surface and its chemical nature. It is for this reason that solid catalysts are used in a finely divided form so as to have a large surface area.

If it is found experimentally that the rate of a reaction depends upon the chemical nature of the containing vessel, or that the rate is altered by changing the surface area (e.g. by adding powdered glass to a reaction taking place in a glass vessel) then it may be deduced that the reaction is heterogeneous.

The most remarkable feature of heterogeneous reactions is the chemical specificity of the solid (catalyst) phase. Not only do different solids produce rates of reaction differing by many powers of ten, but they may also yield different products from the same initial compound. Two examples of this type of behaviour are shown below for the thermal decomposition of ethanol and formic acid

$$C_2H_5OH \xrightarrow{\text{alumina}} C_2H_4 + H_2O$$

$$C_2H_5OH \xrightarrow{\text{copper}} CH_3CHO + H_2$$

$$HCOOH \xrightarrow{\text{alumina}} H_2O + CO$$

$$HCOOH \xrightarrow{\text{copper}} H_2 + CO_2$$

These examples demonstrate the fact that the catalyst

cannot function merely by concentrating the reacting gas in the surface layer and so increasing the rate of reaction at the surface. The formation of different products shows that the surface atoms of the solid are involved in the reaction mechanism.

The role of the solid surface in chemical reactions was explained by Langmuir in 1916. He suggested that the adsorbed molecules were held to catalytic surfaces by chemical bonds. This process is nowadays referred to as 'chemisorption'. It contrasts with physical adsorption in which the molecules are held to the surface by weak van der Waal's forces of attraction. Chemisorption is characterized by a high heat of adsorption (20 kcal to 200 kcal) which is comparable to the heat evolved in a chemical change. Indeed the heat of adsorption of the first fraction of oxygen onto charcoal is over twice the heat of combustion of carbon. This is because no work has to be done to break the carbon-carbon lattice in forming a surface compound and so more heat is evolved than in combustion.

Another striking feature of chemisorption is that it can occur at temperatures far above the boiling point of the adsorbed substance (e.g. ammonia on tungsten at 800°C) which again points strongly to firm bonding between the surface and the gas.

If the adsorbed gas is chemisorbed, there is a certain limiting amount of gas that can be held on the surface. Langmuir concluded that this limit is reached when the surface is covered by a layer one molecule thick.

Using the idea that there is a dynamic rather than a static equilibrium between the adsorbed gas and the gas in the bulk phase, it is possible to deduce a relationship between the fraction of the surface covered and the pressure of the gas at constant temperature. This is called the Langmuir Adsorption Isotherm.

Let p = pressure of the gas

θ = fraction of surface covered by gas

then $1 - \theta$ = fraction of uncovered surface

If a dynamic equilibrium is set up then

rate of evaporation = rate of adsorption   8.1

The rate of evaporation depends only on the amount of gas already adsorbed, which is proportional to θ. Using (M1),

rate of evaporation = $k_1\theta$ 8.2

The rate of adsorption is proportional to the area of uncovered surface and to the pressure in the gas phase, since the pressure determines the number of collisions between gas molecules and solid surface per unit area.

Hence,   rate of adsorption = $k_2(1-\theta)p$ 8.3

Using the fact that rate of evaporation equals rate of adsorption (8.1),

$$\boxed{k_1\theta = k_2(1-\theta)p}$$ 8.4

Equation (8.4), which refers to the adsorption of a single gas at a constant temperature, is known as the *Langmuir Adsorption Isotherm*. It may be used to deduce the order of simple heterogeneous reactions if it is assumed that the rate of reaction is proportional to the amount of adsorbed gas.

There are three special cases of (8.4) which are of kinetic importance.

Case 1. *The adsorption is slight*

In this case, θ is much less than unity and so $(1-\theta)$ is nearly equal to unity (8.4) then becomes

$$k_1\theta = k_2p$$ 8.5

i.e. the amount of adsorbed gas is proportional to the pressure of the gas.

Since the rate of reaction depends on the amount of adsorbed gas, (8.5) shows that the rate of reaction will be proportional to the pressure of the gas.
Using M1,

$$-\frac{dp}{dt} = kp$$

This is the equation for a first order reaction, k being the rate constant. Some examples of first order heterogeneous reactions of this type are as follows:

$$2AsH_3 \xrightarrow{\quad glass \quad} 2As + 3H_2$$

$$2N_2O \xrightarrow{\quad gold \quad} 2N_2 + O_2$$

$$2HI \xrightarrow{\quad platinum \quad} H_2 + I_2$$

The last two reactions should be noted, because, when occurring homogeneously, they are often quoted as standard examples of second order reactions.

Case 2. *The surface is nearly covered*

In this case θ is almost unity and (8.4) becomes

$$k_1 = k_2(1 - \theta)p$$

Rearranging $\qquad (1 - \theta) = \dfrac{k_1}{k_2 p} \qquad\qquad 8.6$

i.e. the fraction of the surface remaining uncovered is inversely proportional to the pressure of the gas.

This may be illustrated with reference to the catalytic hydrogenation of ethylene on a copper catalyst at $0°C$. It is found experimentally that the rate is directly proportional to the concentration of hydrogen, but inversely proportional to the concentration of ethylene i.e.

$$\text{rate} = \frac{k[H_2]}{[C_2H_4]} \qquad\qquad 8.7$$

From the definition of order of reaction (page 5) (8.7) is a zero order rate law. It may be interpreted by assuming that the hydrogen is slightly adsorbed whereas the ethylene is strongly adsorbed, and covers most of the surface. In this case the rate determining factor will be the adsorption of hydrogen which will depend on the pressure of the hydrogen (from 8.5) and on the fraction of surface *not* covered by ethylene. As seen in (8.6) the latter will be inversely proportional to the pressure of ethylene and so the rate of reaction is proportional to $[H_2]$ and to $1/[C_2H_4]$ in agreement with the experimental result (8.7).

The decomposition of ammonia on platinum is also of this type, the rate being proportional to the pressure of ammonia and inversely proportional to the pressure of hydrogen which is therefore deduced to be strongly adsorbed.

Case 3. The surface is saturated

When this occurs the amount of adsorbed gas is constant and cannot be increased by increasing the pressure. The rate of reaction is therefore constant and a zero order reaction is observed.

Two examples of this type of reaction are the catalytic decomposition of ammonia on tungsten or molybdenum, or the catalytic decomposition of hydrogen iodide on gold.

$$2NH_3 \xrightarrow{\text{tungsten}} N_2 + 3H_2$$
$$2HI \xrightarrow{\text{gold}} H_2 + I_2$$

In zero order reactions of this type, if the pressure is reduced sufficiently a stage will eventually be reached at which the surface is only slightly covered with adsorbed gas and (8.5) will apply. The order of the reaction will therefore change from zero to one on decreasing the pressure. At intermediate pressures, when the surface is fractionally covered, the reaction will have a fractional order.

The above examples show that in suitable cases simple kinetic behaviour may be found in heterogeneous reactions. In general, the situation is more complex since the adsorption may be intermediate between Case 1 and Case 2. Furthermore the products of the reaction may be adsorbed. For example, in the catalytic oxidation of sulphur dioxide on a platinum catalyst (the Contact Process)

$$2SO_2 + O_2 \xrightarrow{\text{platinum}} 2SO_3$$

79

the following rate laws are obeyed.
When sulphur dioxide is in excess

$$\frac{d[SO_3]}{dt} = \frac{k[O_2]}{[SO_3]^{\frac{1}{2}}}$$

When oxygen is in excess

$$\frac{d[SO_3]}{dt} = \frac{k[SO_2]}{[SO_3]^{\frac{1}{2}}}$$

The occurrence of the concentration of sulphur trioxide in the denominator in the rate laws shows that it is being strongly adsorbed and is inhibiting the reaction.

ENERGY OF ACTIVATION OF HETEROGENEOUS REACTIONS

The Arrhenius equation (4.13) describes the effect of temperature on rate constant, irrespective of how this effect is produced. The apparent energy of activation obtained by using the Arrhenius equation does not always measure the difference between the energy of the reactants and of the transition state (the true activation energy).

On increasing the temperature in a heterogeneous reaction, the adsorbed gas will react at a higher rate. But at the same time gas will be desorbed by the increase in temperature which will reduce the increase in rate. As a result the apparent energy of activation will be lower than the true value. It is only for zero order reactions, in which the surface is completely covered that the true and apparent energies of activation are equal.

MECHANISM OF HETEROGENEOUS CATALYSIS

The function of a catalyst is to provide a mechanism of reaction with a lower energy of activation than is found in the corresponding homogeneous reaction, thus making the reaction on the surface faster than that in the gas phase.

A catalyst lowers the energy of activation by adsorbing the gas on certain positions on the surface. If the atoms of the adsorbed molecule are held on two sites whose spacing is slightly greater than their normal bond distance the bond will be stretched and so taken part of the way to the transition state. Thus less energy is needed to activate an adsorbed molecule than to activate a free gas molecule.

The spacing of the adsorbing sites on a catalyst surface is very critical, which explains why chemically similar substances can have completely different catalytic properties.

The data in TABLE 5 below, in which the energies of activation of corresponding homogeneous and heterogeneous reactions are given, illustrate the lowering of activation energy by a catalyst.

TABLE 5

Reaction	Catalyst	Energy of activation kcal (Heterogeneous)	(Homogeneous)
$2HI \rightarrow H_2 + I_2$	Platinum	14·0	44·0
$2N_2O \rightarrow 2N_2 + O_2$	Gold	29·0	58·5
$2NH_3 \rightarrow N_2 + 3H_2$	Tungsten	39·0	80
$CH_4 \rightarrow C + 2H_2$	Platinum	55	80

It must be stressed that the above treatment is based on the assumption that the solid surface is uniform. This is very seldom the case.

Active site theory

From his study of catalysed reactions, H. S. Taylor developed the 'active site theory' in which it is postulated that the solid surface is not uniform, and that a catalysed chemical reaction can occur only on a few specially favoured sites. On the other hand, adsorption of gas can occur over the whole surface, so that the majority of adsorbed gas may be held on non-active sites. The rate of reaction will be proportional to the amount of gas adsorbed on to the active sites.

Strong evidence for this theory comes from an investigation of the 'poisoning' of catalysts, in which a trace of added substance removes the catalytic activity. Thus in the hydrogenation of ethylene to ethane, on a copper catalyst, a trace of mercury (far less than that required to form a layer one atom thick on the surface) is sufficient to inhibit the reaction. This is because the mercury is preferentially adsorbed on the active sites.

Even more striking is the fact that a catalyst may be 'poisoned' with respect to one reaction and yet capable of catalysing another. For example, colloidal platinum will catalyse the hydrogenation of ketones and of aromatic nitro-compounds. Small amounts of carbon disulphide will prevent the hydrogenation of ketones but the partially poisoned platinum is still capable of catalysing the hydrogenation of nitrobenzene. Further small additions of carbon disulphide completely remove the catalytic activity.

Further evidence for the non-uniformity of catalyst surfaces comes from the effect of sintering. Many catalysts can be completely deactivated by heating to a temperature below their melting point. Heating will tend to make the surface atoms more mobile and will thus tend to even out local distortions of the surface, including those distortions which constitute the active sites. Part of the reduction in catalytic power on heating can be accounted for by the fact that the surface area of the catalyst tends to decrease on sintering, so that less gas is adsorbed. Nevertheless, the loss in catalytic activity can be many times greater than would be produced by the reduction in surface area.

Kinetic studies also lead to the conclusion that catalytic surfaces are non-uniform. An investigation of the reaction

$$CO_2 + H_2 \rightarrow CO + H_2O$$

on a platinum surface, shows that when an excess of carbon dioxide is used it slows down the reaction. The kinetics of the reaction are described by the equation

$$\text{rate} \propto \frac{\text{partial pressure of hydrogen}}{\text{partial pressure of carbon dioxide}} \qquad 8.8$$

An examination of (8.6) shows that the above result implies that the carbon dioxide is strongly adsorbed and covers most of the surface, and that the rate is determined by the adsorption of hydrogen on that small part of the surface not covered by carbon dioxide. However, direct measurements of the amounts of carbon dioxide and hydrogen adsorbed on the platinum catalyst show that far more hydrogen is adsorbed than carbon dioxide.

These results can be easily explained on the active site theory if equation (8.8) is interpreted as meaning that the carbon dioxide is preferentially adsorbed on the active sites, which are only a small fraction of the total surface. The amount of hydrogen adsorbed on the non-active sites can thus be much greater than the amount of carbon dioxide adsorbed on the active sites.

It is interesting to compare the rates of decomposition of formic acid on various surfaces, shown in TABLE 6.

TABLE 6. $H \cdot COOH \rightarrow H_2 + CO_2$

Surface	Energy of activation (kcal)	Relative rate
Glass	24·5	1
Gold	23·5	40
Silver	31·0	40
Platinum	22·0	2000
Rhodium	25·0	10000

Thus on glass and rhodium the rates differ by a factor of ten thousand while the energies of activation are almost equal. This could reasonably be interpreted by assuming that rhodium has far more active sites per unit area than has glass.

A quantitative theory of heterogeneous catalysis has not yet been developed. This is not surprising in view of the complex nature of the solid surface. However, the application of the simple idea of a monomolecular layer of chemisorbed gas on the surface, combined with the Langmuir isotherm, does enable an account to be given of the kinetics of heterogeneous reactions in simple cases.

9

CHAIN REACTIONS

So far we have only considered reactions in which the reagents were normal molecules or ions. In some reaction mechanisms however, a third type of molecular species, known as a *free radical*, plays a predominant role.

A free radical is a molecule or ion which possesses one or more unpaired electrons. In addition, it is usual to restrict the term 'free radical' to those substances in which the unpaired electron gives rise to high chemical reactivity. The following are typical examples of free radicals. The unpaired electron is denoted by a dot.

H·	atomic hydrogen
HO·	hydroxyl
CH_3·	methyl
CH_3CO·	acetyl

Free radicals cannot be prepared in the pure state at high concentrations because of their tendency to recombine to form a normal molecule. Molecules like oxygen, nitric oxide and nitrogen dioxide contain unpaired electrons, but are not usually classified as free radicals since they are stable in the pure state, and are not abnormally reactive.

From a kinetic viewpoint the important features of free radicals are:

(a) their high reactivity can bring about reactions which cannot be readily accomplished by stable molecules.

(b) in the reaction of a free radical with a molecule, one or more free radicals are among the products.

The reason for (b) is that a normal molecule contains an even number of electrons, whereas a free radical almost always contains an odd number of electrons. An odd number plus an even number always gives an odd number. Hence when a free radical reacts with a normal molecule, the products must contain an odd number of electrons, i.e. a free radical is formed. Atomic oxygen, however, has an even number of electrons and so can react with a normal molecule (for instance, hydrogen) to form two free radicals (see 9.14), since the sum of two odd numbers is an even number.

A *chain reaction* consists of a series of consecutive reactions in which a product molecule of one stage becomes a reactant in the next stage. This molecule is known as a *chain carrier*, of which the most common type is a free radical. Chain reactions are further classified as *stationary* or *branched* depending on whether one or more chain carriers are formed for each chain carrier that reacts.

It might at this point be noted that branched and stationary chain reactions occur as a result of nuclear fission, for example in atomic piles and in atomic bombs. These, however, are nuclear and not chemical processes and are not within the scope of this book.

The idea that chemical reactions can occur by chain mechanisms was first suggested by Bodenstein in 1913. This was verified by Paneth in 1929 who showed that free radicals exist as intermediates in the thermal decomposition of organic substances. As will be seen later this is strong evidence for a chain mechanism.

A diagrammatic representation of Paneth's apparatus is shown in FIGURE 8.

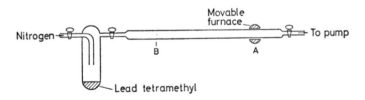

FIGURE 8. Metallic mirror technique

A movable electric furnace, maintaining a temperature of 450°C, was initially at position A. On passing the nitrogen saturated with lead tetramethyl through the furnace a lead mirror was deposited at A. When the furnace was moved to position B a new lead mirror was formed at B while the lead mirror at A gradually disappeared. It was found that the mirror at A could be removed when B was up to 30 cm away from A. Cooling the tube between A and B did not affect the removal of the mirror.

The explanation of these results is that, on first heating, the reaction

$$Pb(CH_3)_4 \rightarrow Pb + 4CH_3\cdot$$

occurs at A. The resultant methyl radicals in the gas stream are then capable of reacting with lead at low temperatures to reform lead tetramethyl. Thus when the furnace is moved to B the methyl radicals formed are carried to A and remove the lead mirror previously deposited there.

It was subsequently found that if organic vapours, e.g. acetaldehyde, were passed through the furnace the resultant gases could also remove metallic mirrors and by condensing the vapours in a cold trap, metal-alkyls could be isolated. The explanation in the case of acetaldehyde is that the first stage of the decomposition is

$$CH_3CHO \rightarrow CH_3\cdot + \cdot CHO$$

which produces the free radicals that remove the metallic mirror.

The role of free radicals in promoting chain reactions is best seen by considering definite examples. One of the simplest is the reaction of hydrogen with chlorine. In the dark at s.t.p. the reaction is very slow, but in sunlight reaction occurs quite rapidly according to the overall equation.

$$H_2 + Cl_2 \rightarrow 2HCl$$

From the low rate of reaction in the dark it may be concluded that hydrogen and chlorine *molecules* do not readily react together. The mechanism suggested by Nernst (1918) is

$$Cl_2 \xrightarrow{\text{light}} Cl\cdot + Cl\cdot \qquad 9.1$$

$$Cl\cdot + H_2 \longrightarrow HCl + H\cdot \qquad 9.2$$

$$H\cdot + Cl_2 \longrightarrow HCl + Cl\cdot \qquad 9.3$$

The Cl· formed in (9.3) can then react with another hydrogen molecule, and so a continuous chain of reaction can be brought about by one initial free radical. This chain will continue until either

(a) all the hydrogen or all the chlorine is used up, or

(b) free radicals are destroyed by recombination, e.g.

$$H\cdot + H\cdot \rightarrow H_2 \qquad 9.4$$

$$H\cdot + Cl\cdot \rightarrow HCl \qquad 9.5$$

$$Cl\cdot + Cl\cdot \rightarrow Cl_2 \qquad 9.6$$

Equations (9.1) to (9.6) illustrate the three essential processes of any chain reaction. These are:

Initiation, in which free radicals are formed from normal molecules, either by chemical reaction, thermal decomposition or absorption of radiation. (As in (9.1)).

Propagation, in which the free radical reacts with a molecule, forming amongst the products at least one new free radical. (As in (9.2) and (9.3)).

Termination, in which the radicals recombine to give normal molecules. (As in (9.4), (9.5) and (9.6)).

At first sight it might be expected that termination reactions would occur easily as the free radicals could reform stable molecules. But it is important to bear in mind the principle of conservation of energy. The reaction $H_2 \rightarrow H\cdot + H\cdot$ is highly endothermic (108 kcal). Conversely if two hydrogen atoms recombine, this quantity of heat will be liberated. Suppose now that two hydrogen atoms recombine far away from other molecules or the walls of the vessel. The molecule formed will possess this amount of

energy which is precisely the energy of dissociation. It wi...
therefore be unstable and will be able to redissociate into
atoms at its first vibration.

It may be concluded from this argument that radical
recombination will only occur if a third body is present to
take up some of the energy liberated in the recombination.
This third body is usually an atom in the surface of the
walls of the vessel or another molecule in the gas phase. The
latter possibility requires a three body collision which can
be shown by the kinetic theory of gases to be improbable at
low pressures. Hence free radicals in the gas phase can have
a life far longer than the time between collisions.

Proof of the chain nature of the reaction between
hydrogen and chlorine comes from two other sources.
Firstly, by measuring the quantity of light absorbed, it was
found that 10^4 to 10^6 molecules of HCl are formed for each
photon absorbed. The role of light in this reaction is clearly
that of an initiator leading to a chain reaction

$$Cl_2 + light \rightarrow Cl\cdot + Cl\cdot$$

The resultant chlorine atoms start off chains as in (9.2)
and (9.3).

The second method is due to Polanyi who used the
apparatus shown diagrammatically in FIGURE 9. Hydrogen,

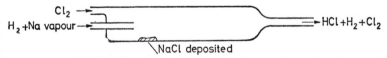

FIGURE 9. Polanyi's apparatus (diagrammatic)

which had been passed over molten sodium, was
allowed to mix with chlorine and the amounts of sodium
chloride and hydrogen chloride formed were measured.
It was found that

$$\frac{\text{molecules of HCl formed}}{\text{molecules of NaCl formed}} \simeq 10,000$$

c interpretation is as follows:

$$Na + Cl_2 \rightarrow NaCl + Cl\cdot$$

$$Cl\cdot + H_2 \rightarrow HCl + H\cdot$$

$$H\cdot + Cl_2 \rightarrow HCl + Cl\cdot$$

Thus each sodium atom forms one free radical which initiates a chain reaction.

The kinetics of chain reactions are necessarily complex but in some cases a simple order of reaction may result. An example is the thermal decomposition of diethyl ether

$$C_2H_5OC_2H_5 \rightarrow C_2H_6 + CH_3CHO$$

which obeys first order kinetics. The mechanism of this reaction[1] has four stages and involves two free radicals and is too complicated to discuss here. However, the thermal decomposition of acetaldehyde has a comparatively simple mechanism which can be shown to lead to an order of 1·5, as found by experiment. The mechanism is

Initiation $\qquad CH_3CHO \xrightarrow{k_1} CH_3\cdot + CHO \qquad$ 9.7

Propagation $CH_3CHO + CH_3\cdot \xrightarrow{k_2} CH_4 + CO + CH_3\cdot$ 9.8

Termination $\qquad 2CH_3\cdot \xrightarrow{k_3} C_2H_6 \qquad$ 9.9

$$2CHO\cdot \xrightarrow{k_4} 2CO + H_2$$

where the k's are the rate constants for the various stages of the reaction. The overall reaction is mainly

$$CH_3CHO \rightarrow CH_4 + CO$$

although traces of C_2H_6 and H_2 are formed.

If the reaction proceeds at a steady rate it may be assumed that the rate of formation of methyl radicals in (9.7) is

---

[1] C. N. Hinshelwood, 'Kinetics of Chemical Change', Oxford University Press, 1947, p. 89–92.

equal to the rate of their destruction in (9.9), since the concentration of CH_3· is unaffected by (9.8). This follows from the stationary state hypothesis (see page 57).

$$\text{rate of formation} = k_1[CH_3CHO]$$
$$= k_3[CH_3\text{·}]^2 = \text{rate of destruction} \quad 9.10$$

whence $[CH_3\text{·}] = \left\{\dfrac{k_1}{k_3}[CH_3CHO]\right\}^{\frac{1}{2}}$

(by re-arranging (9.10)).

Since the rate of formation of product is governed by (9.8)

$$\text{overall rate} = k_2[CH_3CHO][CH_3\text{·}]$$

$$= k_2\left(\dfrac{k_1}{k_3}\right)^{\frac{1}{2}}[CH_3CHO]^{3/2} \quad 9.11$$

e reaction is therefore of order 3/2.

Free radicals have been detected in the thermal decomositions of both diethyl ether and acetaldehyde. Since the observed orders of reaction agree with those predicted by free radical mechanisms, it may be concluded that both these decompositions are chain reactions.

Chain reactions can also occur in the liquid phase and are the basis of many industrial processes for forming polymers. A common example is the polymerization of molecules of the form $RCH=CH_2$ according to the following equations, where R is a substituent group in the ethylene molecule and X· is a free radical.

$$X\text{·} + RCH=CH_2 \rightarrow RXCHCH_2\text{·}$$
$$RXCHCH_2\text{·} + RCH=CH_2 \rightarrow RXCHCH_2RCHCH_2\text{·}$$

This process can be repeated n times to give

$$RXCHCH_2(RCHCH_2)_n\text{·}$$

Eventually the chain is terminated by radical recombination. Some examples of industrially important polymers are shown in TABLE 7 below which deals with the polymerization of ethylene molecules, mono-substituted by the group R.

TABLE 7

R	Polymer
H	Polythene
CH_3	Polypropylene
Cl	Polyvinyl chloride (p.v.c.)
$OCOCH_3$	Polyvinyl acetate (p.v.a.)
C_6H_5	Polystyrene

Perspex and Teflon are also polymerized ethylene derivatives, the monomers being methyl methacrylate and tetrafluoroethylene respectively.

The kinetics of such reactions are complex, but their mechanisms all involve the common features of initiation, propagation and termination, which are characteristic of chain reactions.

Initiation of chain reactions can be brought about by irradiation with ultra-violet light or gamma rays or by chemical methods. The addition of benzoyl peroxide or Fenton's reagent yields free radicals according to the equations

$$C_6H_5COOOH \rightarrow C_6H_5COO\cdot + \cdot OH$$

$$Fe^{2+} + H_2O_2 \rightarrow Fe^{3+} + \cdot OH + OH^-$$

IDENTIFICATION OF CHAIN REACTIONS

The following methods may be used to determine whether a reaction follows a chain mechanism

1. *Inhibitors*

If a small amount of an added substance, such as nitric oxide or propylene produces a large decrease in the rate of reaction, a chain reaction may be suspected. The inhibitor is a molecule that can react with and remove free radicals, for example

$$CH_3\cdot + \cdot NO \rightarrow CH_3NO \rightarrow H_2O + HCN$$

Nitric oxide is an effective inhibitor and a partial pressure of 1 to 2 mm may reduce the rate of reaction by a factor of 10 to 100 or even stop it altogether. The reason is that a nitric oxide molecule removes a free radical and so prevents the starting of a chain. Propylene also acts as an inhibitor in gas reactions, being itself polymerized in the process.

Benzoquinone is an effective inhibitor of liquid-phase polymerization reactions.

The term 'negative catalyst' is sometimes used for inhibitors. This is not desirable as the inhibitor reacts irreversibly with the free radical in carrying out its function whereas a catalyst is still in its original form at the end of the reaction.

2. *Metallic mirror technique*

If the gaseous products of reaction are capable of removing metallic mirrors, forming metal alkyls, then it may be concluded that free radicals are present and a chain mechanism is likely.

3. *Physical methods*

In some cases free radicals may be detected directly by physical methods, e.g. spectroscopy, mass spectrometry and electron spin resonance. The existence of free radicals is again evidence of a chain mechanism.

BRANCHED CHAIN REACTIONS

These are reactions in which, at some stage, more than one free radical is produced for each free radical consumed. The combustion of hydrogen and hydrocarbons in air or oxygen frequently gives rise to branched chain reactions. This will be illustrated by considering the reaction of hydrogen and oxygen to form water at 500°C to 600°C.

Initiation $\quad W + H_2 \quad \rightarrow H\cdot + H\cdot$ $\qquad$ 9.12

where W refers to an inert atom on the walls of the vessel.

Branching $\quad H\cdot + O_2 \quad \rightarrow \cdot OH + O\cdot$ $\qquad$ 9.13

$\qquad\quad O\cdot + H_2 \quad \rightarrow \cdot OH + H\cdot$ $\qquad$ 9.14

Propagation $\quad \cdot OH + H_2 \quad \rightarrow H_2O + H\cdot \qquad$ 9.15

$\qquad\qquad\quad H\cdot + O_2 \quad \rightarrow HO_2\cdot \qquad\qquad$ 9.16

$\qquad\qquad\quad HO_2\cdot + H_2 \rightarrow H_2O + \cdot OH \qquad$ 9.17

Termination $\quad$ Radicals $\quad \rightarrow$ inactive products at walls of vessel

The special feature of this mechanism is the two branching reactions (9.13) and (9.14) in which the number of free radicals doubles. This makes possible a rapid increase in rate of reaction which will lead to explosion unless the termination processes can destroy the extra free radicals as fast as they are produced. A high temperature is necessary to bring about reaction because of the difficulty of producing hydrogen atoms from hydrogen molecules by direct heating.

On the other hand, the reaction of hydrogen and oxygen can occur explosively at room temperature on sparking. The spark produces a local 'hot spot' which produces sufficient free radicals to trigger off the branched chain.

At first sight it may not appear likely that, by starting with a few free radicals and continuously doubling their number, an explosion should be produced. The following story illustrates the effect of continuous doubling in tangible terms.

It is said that in ancient times a Pharaoh was taught to play chess and was so pleased with the game that he offered his tutor a reward. The tutor demanded one grain of wheat for the first square on the board, two for the second, four for the third, eight for the fourth and so on for all 64 squares. This seemed a modest prize and was agreed to by the Pharaoh. However, when the quantity of wheat is calculated $[(2^{64} - 1)$ grains] it comes to about a million million tons! In a gas at s.t.p. an individual molecule would suffer 64 collisions in less than a millionth of a second. If each collision resulted in branching an explosion would certainly occur.

The oxidation of hydrocarbons (of importance in internal

combustion engines) is also a branched chain process, the initial stage being

Initiation $\qquad RH + O_2 \rightarrow HO_2\cdot + R\cdot$

Propagation $\qquad RO_2\cdot + RH \rightarrow RO_2H + R\cdot$

Branching $\qquad RO_2H \left\langle \begin{array}{l} OH\cdot + \text{organic radical} \\ \text{molecular oxidation products} \end{array} \right.$

The function of lead tetraethyl as an antiknock in petrol is to control the number of free radicals by providing a catalytic surface on which radicals can recombine. Many processes of combustion are also branched chain reactions.

The mathematical treatment of the kinetics of branched chain reactions is too complex to be dealt with here.

10

WORKED EXAMPLES

1. *Calculation of a first order rate constant from the differential rate law*

The method is illustrated using data taken from the decomposition of benzene diazonium chloride[1] in water at 40°C.

$$C_6H_5N_2Cl + H_2O \rightarrow C_6H_5OH + HCl + N_2$$

The reaction was followed by measuring the increase in pressure, due to the evolution of nitrogen, by means of a xylene manometer. Consequently, the amount of reaction is expressed in terms of centimetres of xylene. The experimental results are shown in TABLE 8 below. p represents the increase in pressure due to the evolved nitrogen. p_∞ is the final pressure after infinite time.

TABLE 8

t min	p cm xylene	$p_\infty - p$	$\log(p_\infty - p)$
0	0	22·62	1·3545
2	1·07	21·55	1·3334
4	2·15	20·47	1·3111
8	4·14	18·48	1·2667
12	5·89	16·73	1·2235
16	7·52	15·10	1·1790
20	9·00	13·62	1·1342
24	10·32	12·30	1·0899
28	11·52	11·10	1·0453
35	13·33	9·29	0·9680
40	14·47	8·15	0·9112
45	15·42	7·20	0·8573
50	16·28	6·34	0·8021
60	17·74	4·88	0·6884
68	18·60	4·02	0·6042
infinity	22·62	—	—

[1] E. A. Moelwyn-Hughes and P. Johnson, *Trans. Faraday Soc.* 1940, 36, 950.

The rate law for a first order reaction (2.6) is

$$\frac{\mathrm{d}x}{\mathrm{d}t} = k(a - x)$$

k may be calculated from this equation by substituting into it numerical values of $\mathrm{d}x/\mathrm{d}t$ and $(a - x)$ at a given time. In this experiment, the fraction of reaction is proportional to the increase in pressure (p). The initial concentration (a) is proportional to p_∞ and, therefore, the concentration remaining at time t, i.e. $(a - x)$, is proportional to $(p_\infty - p)$. For a first order reaction, any units may be used to measure concentration since, from (2.10), k depends on a *ratio* of two concentrations, the ratio being dimensionless. This justifies the use of cm xylene as the unit of concentration in FIGURE 10.

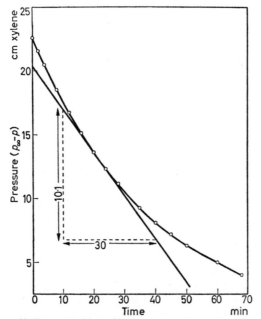

FIGURE 10. Decomposition of benzene diazonium chloride at 40·0°C

97

Using the data in TABLE 8, a graph of $(a - x)$ against t has been plotted in FIGURE 10, and a tangent has been drawn to the curve at $t = 20$ min.

Slope of graph $= \dfrac{\mathrm{d}(a - x)}{\mathrm{d}t} = \dfrac{-\mathrm{d}x}{\mathrm{d}t}$

$$= -\frac{10\cdot1}{30} = -0\cdot337 \text{ cm xylene min}^{-1}$$

At this time $(a - x)$ equals $13\cdot62$ cm xylene. Substituting in (2.6)

$$k = \frac{1}{(a - x)}\frac{\mathrm{d}x}{\mathrm{d}t} = \frac{0\cdot337}{13\cdot62} = 0\cdot0247 \text{ min}^{-1}$$

This value may be compared with that obtained from the integrated rate law (2.10)

$$kt = \ln\frac{a}{(a - x)}$$

In FIGURE 11, $\log(p_\infty - p)$ is plotted against time. The result is a straight line of slope $-0\cdot556/50$ min^{-1} (see M2). From (2.9), using M3 and M17 the slope equals $-k/2\cdot303$.

Therefore $k = \dfrac{2\cdot303 \times 0\cdot556}{50} = 0\cdot0256$ min^{-1}.

Reasonable agreement has been obtained from these two methods. The first method is quite unreliable, however, if there is any appreciable experimental error, as it is extremely difficult to draw a good tangent to an irregular curve.

2. *Calculation of a first order rate constant from conductivity measurements*

The hydrolysis of tertiary amyl iodide in aqueous ethanol is a convenient reaction to study conductometrically.

$$t\text{–}C_5H_{11}I + H_2O \rightarrow t\text{–}C_5H_{11}OH + H^+ + I^-$$

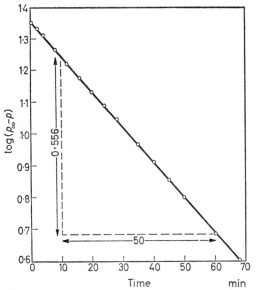

FIGURE 11. Decomposition of benzene diazonium chloride at 40·0°C

In this reaction the concentration of ions increases with time. In dilute solutions, the conductivity is proportional to the concentration of ions; consequently the increase in conductivity is proportional to the amount of reaction.

The experiment is carried out by preparing an approximately 0·02 molar solution of *t*–amyl bromide in aqueous ethanol, the conductivity of which is measured at various times with any convenient cell It is not necessary to know the cell constant, since first order rate constants depend on a *ratio* of concentrations (2.10).

The results obtained in an experiment using 80 per cent aqueous ethanol as solvent at 25°C are shown in TABLE 9.

The rate law for a first order reaction (2.10) is

$$kt = \ln \frac{a}{a - x}$$

99

TABLE 9

t min	$10^3 \times C$ ohm^{-1}	$10^3 \times (C_\infty - C)$ ohm^{-1}	$\log[10^3 \times (C_\infty - C)]$
0	0·39	10·11	1·005
1·5	1·78	8·72	0·941
4·5	4·09	6·41	0·807
9·0	6·32	4·18	0·621
16·0	8·36	2·14	0·330
22·0	9·34	1·16	0·065
'infinity'	10·50	0·00	—

Let $C°$ = initial conductivity

C = conductivity at time t

C_∞ = conductivity at infinite time

The change in conductivity produced by complete reaction is proportional to the initial concentration of the t-amyl iodide

i.e. $$a \propto C_\infty - C°$$

Similarly, the concentration (x) that has reacted at time is proportional to the change in conductivity at that time

$$x \propto C - C°$$

By subtraction,

$$a - x \propto C_\infty - C$$

From (2.9) $$\ln a - \ln (a - x) = kt$$

From M3, a graph of $\ln (a - x)$ against t will give a straight line of slope $-k$.

Using M16, since $(C_\infty - C)$ is proportional to $(a - x)$, a graph of $\ln (C_\infty - C)$ against t gives the same slope, namely $-k$.

In FIGURE 12, a graph is shown of $\log (C_\infty - C)$ against t. Since common logarithms are used the slope (from M17) is $-k/2·303$.

From FIGURE 12 the slope is $-0·83/20 = -0·0415$ min^{-1} (See M2).

Hence $k = 2·303 \times 0·0415 = 0·095$ min^{-1}.

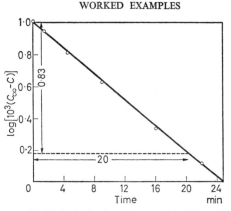

FIGURE 12. Hydrolysis of tertiary amyl iodide at 25·0°C

It may be noted that at no stage in the calculation is the actual value of concentration of reactant required. All that is needed is a parameter that is proportional to concentration. The above method may therefore be used in cases where the reaction rate has been followed by measuring the pressure of evolved gas, or the change in optical rotation or in optical density of a solution.

3. Second order reaction with equal initial concentrations of reactants

The graphical determination of the second order rate constant by the method on page 14 is shown for the reaction[1] of ethyl p–nitrobenzoate with sodium hydroxide in aqueous acetone (40 per cent by volume) at 15·2°C.

$$p\text{–NO}_2\text{·}C_6H_4\text{·}CO_2C_2H_5 + NaOH \rightarrow p\text{–NO}_2\text{·}C_6H_4\text{·}COONa + C_2H_5OH$$

The reaction is rapid (half-life 4·1 minutes) and so a special technique was used to reduce timing errors on mixing the reactants. The method employed was to seal 5·00 ml of decinormal sodium hydroxide solution in a thin-walled

[1] W. B. S. Newling and C. N. Hinshelwood, *J. Chem. Soc.*, 1936, 1358.

glass tube which was placed in a larger and thicker glass tube containing 5·00 ml of a decinormal solution of the ethyl p–nitrobenzoate. When temperature equilibrium had been achieved, the inner tube was broken and the contents of the outer tube were stirred rapidly. At the end of the required time, the reaction was 'frozen' by pouring the contents of the larger tube into a known excess of standard acid, which was subsequently back-titrated with standard alkali. The rate of acid hydrolysis is negligible at 15·2°C.

The experimental results are shown in TABLE 10.

TABLE 10

Time (sec)	[NaOH] $(a - x)$	x	$\dfrac{x}{(a - x)}$	k
0	0·0500	0·0000	0·000	—
120	0·0335	0·0165	0·492	0·0819
180	0·0291	0·0209	0·718	0·0796
240	0·0256	0·0244	0·953	0·0794
330	0·0209	0·0291	1·381	0·0839
530	0·0155	0·0345	2·226	0·0840
600	0·0148	0·0352	2·378	0·0792

The concentration (mole litre^{-1}) of sodium hydroxide shown in TABLE 10 will also be the concentration of the ethyl p–nitrobenzoate, since the initial concentrations are equal.

The differential rate law (2.13) is

$$\frac{\mathrm{d}x}{\mathrm{d}t} = k(a - x)^2.$$

The corresponding integrated form (2.15) is

$$kt = \frac{x}{a(a - x)}$$

In FIGURE 13, $x/(a - x)$ is plotted against t. The slope of the graph is $2·06/500 = 4·12 \times 10^{-3}$ sec^{-1} (See M2).

From (2.15) the slope is ak, and since $a = 0·0500$ mole litre^{-1}

$$k = \frac{4·12 \times 10^{-3}}{0·0500} = 0·0824 \text{ litre mole}^{-1} \text{ sec}^{-1}$$

102

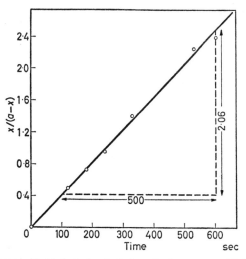

FIGURE 13. Hydrolysis of ethyl p–nitrobenzoate at 15·2°C

The values of k found by direct substitution in (2.15) are also shown in TABLE 10. The average value is 0·0813 litre mole⁻¹ sec⁻¹, in good agreement with the graphical value.

4. *Calculation of second order rate constants when the reactants are at different initial concentrations.*

The method is illustrated by the reaction[1] of n-amyl fluoride and sodium ethoxide

$$n–C_5H_{11}F + NaOC_2H_5 \rightarrow NaF + n–C_5H_{11}OC_2H_5$$

at 120·0°C in 99·9 per cent ethanol. Since ethanol boils at 78°C the sealed tube technique must be used, and the high temperature of the experiment requires a correction for solvent expansion to be made. The experimental results are shown in TABLE 11. The reaction was followed by adding excess hydrochloric acid (0·3700 N) and back-titrating with standard sodium hydroxide solution. Each sealed tube

---

[1] J. L. Latham, Ph.D. Thesis, University of London, 1951, p. 46.

contained 4·07 ml of reaction mixture (at 20°C) and so concentrations are conveniently measured in ml of 0·3700N hydrochloric acid per 4·07 ml aliquot of reaction mixture.

The initial concentration of the sodium ethoxide in the reaction mixture was found by direct titration of an aliquot with the hydrochloric acid. The value found was 5·93 ml of 0·3700N HCl giving an initial molarity of

$$\frac{5·93 \times 0·3700}{4·07} = 0·539$$

The initial molarity of the n–amyl fluoride was found by weighing a sample into a 100 ml volumetric flask and diluting to the mark with sodium ethoxide solution. The value so obtained was 0·432 moles litre^{-1}. An aliquot of 4·07 ml is equivalent to

$$\frac{0·432 \times 4·07}{0·3700} = 4·75 \text{ ml of HCl}$$

TABLE 11

Time $\times 10^{-4}$ (sec) t	Sodium ethoxide $(a-x)$	n–Amyl fluoride $(b-x)$	$\frac{b(a-x)}{a(b-x)}$	$\log\frac{b(a-x)}{a(b-x)}$	$k \times 10^5$
0·00	5·93	4·75	1·0000	0·00000	—
1·59	5·47	4·29	1·0213	0·00915	1·24
3·30	5·07	3·89	1·0437	0·01860	1·25
5·14	4·68	3·50	1·0710	0·02978	1·27
8·16	4·17	2·99	1·1174	0·04817	1·28
10·25	3·88	2·70	1·1511	0·06110	1·29
13·04	3·63	2·45	1·1871	0·07451	1·24
17·33	3·26	2·08	1·2552	0·09868	1·23

Since one molecule of n–amyl fluoride removes one molecule of sodium ethoxide, the *difference* between the two concentrations remains constant at $(5·93 - 4·75) = 1·18$ ml of 0·3700N HCl per 4·07 ml aliquot. The concentration of n–amyl fluoride $(b-x)$ shown in TABLE 11 is therefore obtained by subtracting 1·18 from the corresponding sodium ethoxide concentration.

The differential rate law for unequal concentrations (2.17) is

$$\frac{\mathrm{d}x}{\mathrm{d}t} = k(a - x)(b - x)$$

The integrated form (2.22) is

$$kt = \frac{1}{(a - b)} \ln \left[\frac{b(a - x)}{a(b - x)} \right]$$

The calculation of the rate constant from this equation is set out in TABLE 11. Since the logarithmic bracket $[b(a - x)/a(b - x)]$ contains only ratios of concentrations, the values of $(a - x)$ and $(b - x)$ can be expressed in ml of 0·3700N HCl. However, the term $1/(a - b)$ has dimensions of (concentration)$^{-1}$, and so $(a - b)$ must be expressed in mole litre^{-1} to give the second order rate constant (k) with dimensions of litre mole^{-1} sec^{-1}. The rate constant is obtained by the multiplication of the logarithmic term by $2·303/(a - b)t$ (see M17). Thus for the first value of the rate constant is

$$k = \frac{2·303 \times 0·00915}{(0·539 - 0·432) \times 1·59 \times 10^4} = 1·24 \times 10^{-5}$$

litre mole^{-1} sec^{-1}.

The mean value of k (uncorrected for solvent expansion) is $1·26 \times 10^{-5}$ litre mole^{-1} sec^{-1} at 120·0°C. The solutions were, however, made up at 20°C, and the 100°C rise in temperature causes the ethanol to expand by 14 per cent. The actual concentrations are therefore 14 per cent lower than the nominal values. This does not affect the ratios in the logarithmic bracket, but the term $1/(a - b)$ increases by 14 per cent (i.e. by a factor of 1·14). The corrected rate constant is therefore $1·26 \times 10^{-5} \times 1·14 = 1·44 \times 10^{-5}$ litre mole^{-1} sec^{-1}.

5. *Calculation of energy of activation from kinetic results at two temperatures*

The method is illustrated using data for the hydrolysis of

tertiary butyl bromide[1] in aqueous acetone at 25·0°C and 50·0°C.

$$t\text{–}C_4H_9Br + H_2O \rightarrow t\text{–}C_4H_9OH + HBr$$

The solvent used contained 10 per cent water by volume. The reaction was followed by titrating the liberated acid with standard alkali, after the initial concentration of the t–butyl bromide had been found by weighing. It should be noted that when the initial concentration of reactant is known there is no need to carry out a titration at infinite time, although, if this is done, it provides a useful check on the accuracy of the analytical method.

The experimental results are shown in TABLE 12, in which the concentrations of t–butyl bromide are expressed in mole litre^{-1}. In the table, tertiary butyl bromide has been abbreviated to t–BuBr.

TABLE 12

At 25·0°C			At 50·0°C		
Time hours	[t–BuBr] ($a-x$)	log{$10^2 \times$ [t–BuBr]}	Time min	[t–BuBr] ($a-x$)	log{$10^2 \times$ [t–BuBr]}
0	0·1039	1·017	0	0·1056	1·023
3·15	0·0896	0·952	9	0·0961	0·983
4·10	0·0859	0·934	18	0·0856	0·932
6·20	0·0776	0·890	27	0·0767	0·885
8·20	0·0701	0·846	40	0·0645	0·810
10·00	0·0639	0·806	54	0·0536	0·729
13·5	0·0529	0·724	72	0·0432	0·635
18·3	0·0353	0·548	105	0·0270	0·431
26·0	0·0270	0·431	135	0·0174	0·240
30·8	0·0207	0·316	180	0·0089	−0·051

The order of the reaction is one, and the rate law (2.9)

$$kt = \ln a - \ln(a - x) \text{ is used.}$$

In FIGURE 14 a graph of log $(a - x)$ against t is plotted

---

[1] L. C. Bateman, E. D. Hughes and C. K. Ingold, *J. Chem. Soc.*, 1940, 963.

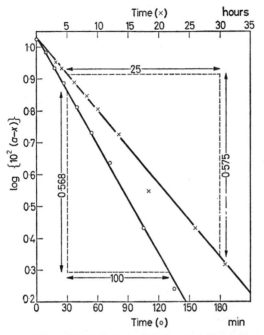

FIGURE 14. Hydrolysis of tertiary butyl bromide

for both temperatures, the top scale being in hours and the bottom scale being in minutes.

Using M3 and M17 the slope of the straight line is $-k/2.303$.

From FIGURE 14, using M2,

slope at 25°C = $-0.575/25 = -0.0230$ hour^{-1}

slope at 50°C = $-0.568/100 = -5.68 \times 10^{-3}$ min^{-1}

Hence k at 25°C = $2.303 \times 0.0230 = 0.0530$ hour^{-1}

k at 50°C = $2.303 \times 5.68 \times 10^{-3} = 1.31 \times 10^{-2}$ min^{-1}

The energy of activation may be found, using (4.13)

$$\ln\left(\frac{k_1}{k_2}\right) = \frac{E}{R}\left(\frac{1}{T_2} - \frac{1}{T_1}\right)$$

Before using this equation the values of k must be converted to the same units, say min^{-1}.

At $25.0°C$, $T_2 = 298.1°K$, $k_2 = 0.0530/60 = 8.83 \times 10^{-4}$ min^{-1}

At $50.0°C$, $T_1 = 323.1°K$, $k_1 = 1.31 \times 10^{-2}$ min^{-1}

Substituting these results in (4.13), using M17

$$2.303 \log \frac{1.31 \times 10^{-2}}{8.83 \times 10^{-4}} = \frac{E}{R}\left(\frac{1}{298.1} - \frac{1}{323.1}\right)$$

Hence

$$\frac{E}{R} = \frac{2.303 \times 1.171 \times 298.1 \times 323.1}{25.0} = 1.039 \times 10^4 °C$$

The numerical value of the perfect gas constant R is 1.987 cal $mole^{-1}$ deg^{-1}

Hence $E = 1.039 \times 10^4 \times 1.987 = 2.06 \times 10^4$ cal $mole^{-1}$

Energy of activation $= 20.6$ kcal $mole^{-1}$.

6. *Calculation of energy of activation from kinetic measurements at several temperatures.*

The decomposition of benzene diazonium chloride in water, discussed in Example 1, has been carefully studied at several temperatures[1]. The experimental results shown in TABLE 13 were obtained by measuring the change in pressure due to the evolution of nitrogen.

TABLE 13

Temperature (°C)	k (sec^{-1})	$T°K$	$10^3/T°K$	$-\log k$
15·1	9.30×10^{-6}	288·2	3·470	5·032
19·9	2.01×10^{-5}	293·0	3·413	4·697
24·7	4.35×10^{-5}	297·8	3·358	4·362
30·0	9.92×10^{-5}	303·1	3·300	4·003
35·0	2.07×10^{-4}	308·1	3·245	3·684
40·1	4.28×10^{-4}	313·2	3·193	3·369
44·9	8.18×10^{-4}	318·0	3·145	3·087

[1] E. A. Moelwyn-Hughes and P. Johnson, *Trans. Faraday Soc.*, 1940, 36, 954.

The activation energy is calculated from these data using the Arrhenius equation (4.9).

$$\ln k = \frac{-E}{RT} + \text{constant}$$

Using M3, a plot of $\ln k$ against $1/T$ will be a straight line of slope $-E/R$. From M17, if common logarithms are used the slope will be $-E/2{\cdot}303R$.

The data in TABLE 13 are plotted in FIGURE 15.

From the graph

$$\text{slope} = \frac{1{\cdot}50}{0{\cdot}25 \times 10^{-3}} = 6{\cdot}00 \times 10^{3}{}^{\circ}\text{C} = \frac{-E}{2{\cdot}303R}$$

Taking R as $1{\cdot}987$ cal mole^{-1} deg^{-1}

$E = 2{\cdot}303 \times 1{\cdot}987 \times 6{\cdot}00 \times 10^{3} = 2{\cdot}74 \times 10^{4}$ cal mole^{-1}

Energy of activation $= 27{\cdot}4$ kcal mole^{-1}.

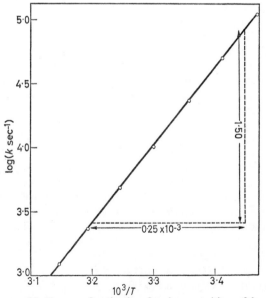

FIGURE 15. Energy of activation for decomposition of benzene diazonium chloride

MATHEMATICAL APPENDIX

This appendix summarizes the mathematical results that have been assumed in derivations and calculations in the preceding chapters.

M1 If x is proportional to y ($x \propto y$) then

$$x = cy, \text{ where } c \text{ is a constant.}$$

2 The numerical value of the slope of a straight line graph of y against x is obtained by choosing two convenient points on the graph, and measuring the differences in values of y and x between the two points, i.e. Δy and Δx. These values must be expressed in the units in which the graph is plotted. The slope is then equal to $\Delta y / \Delta x$.

If the two points have co-ordinates (x_1, y_1) and (x_2, y_2), where x_2 is greater than x_1, then the slope equals $y_2 - y_1 / x_2 - x_1$, which can be either positive or negative. This procedure is illustrated in FIGURES 11, 12, 13, 14 in which time has been plotted along the x-axis.

M3 If $y = mx + c$ (where m and c are constants) a graph of y against x will be a straight line of slope m.

Straight line graphs can often be obtained from more complex expressions by correct choice of the variables to be plotted against one another. Thus if

$$F(x) = \text{a function of } x$$
$$G(y) = \text{a function of } y,$$
then, if $\quad G(y) = mF(x) + c,$

a graph of $G(y)$ plotted against $F(x)$ will also be a

straight line of slope m. This is illustrated in FIGURE 15 where $G(y)$ is $-\log k$ and $F(x)$ is $10^3/T$.

M4 $$X^a \times X^b = X^{a+b}$$

M5 $$X^a \div X^b = X^{a-b}$$

M6 From M5, $X^a \div X^a = X^{a-a} = X^0 = 1$

M7 Factorial X is written as $X!$ As an example,

$$8! = 1 \times 2 \times 3 \times 4 \times 5 \times 6 \times 7 \times 8$$
$$n! = 1 \times 2 \times 3 \times 4 \times \ldots \ldots \times n$$

It can be shown that factorials correspond to the mathematical 'gamma function' of whole numbers, and hence that $0! = 1$.

M8 The exponential e (the base of natural logarithms) is a number equal to $2 \cdot 7183$ (to four places of decimals). e raised to the power of x (e^x) is denoted by exp x. The exponential function may be regarded as the inverse of the logarithmic function.

M9 Analagous to M4 and M5 are the equations

$$\exp(a) \times \exp(b) = \exp(a+b)$$
$$\exp(a) \div \exp(b) = \exp(a-b)$$

M10 Natural logarithms are closely related to the exponential function.

If $$x = \exp(y)$$

then $$\ln x = y$$

M11 The mutual relationship of the logarithmic and exponential function is shown by the equation

$$\exp(\ln x) = x = \ln(\exp x)$$

M12 In common logarithms the exponential number e is replaced by the number ten.

Thus if $y = \log x$, then $x = 10^y$

M13 $$\ln x + \ln y = \ln(xy)$$

M14 $$\ln x - \ln y = \ln (x/y)$$

It should be noted that M13 and M14 are valid also for common logarithms (to the base ten).

M15 If $\ln x = y + c$, where c is a constant then from M10, $x = \exp (y + c)$

Using M9, $x = \exp y \times \exp c$
Since c is a constant, $\exp c$ is also a constant, equal to C, say,
Therefore, $x = C \exp y$

M16 If y is proportional to x, then by M1,

$$y = cx$$

Using M13, $\ln y = \ln c + \ln x$
Since c is a constant, $\ln c$ is a constant.
Hence it follows that if $\ln y$, plotted against another variable, say t, gives a straight line of slope m, then $\ln x$, plotted against t will also give a straight line of slope m. This means that absolute values of y are not required to find the slope m. All that is needed is a quantity proportional to y. This result has been used in Chapter 10, example 2.

M17 Natural and common logarithms are related by the equation
$$\ln x = \ln 10 \times \log x$$

The numerical value of $\ln 10$ is $2 \cdot 303$

Hence $\ln x = 2 \cdot 303 \log x$

M18 The result of differentiating y with respect to x is written as dy/dx. The physical significance of dy/dx is that it represents the slope of the tangent to the curve obtained by plotting a graph of y against x. If a small increase in x produces an increase in y, the curve will have a positive slope and dy/dx will be positive. On the other hand if dy/dx is negative, a small increase in x causes a decrease in y.

M19 If
$$y = x^n$$
$$dy/dx = nx^{n-1}$$

Integration is the reverse of differentiation. The two integrals used in this book are:

M20
$$\int x^n dx = \frac{x^{n+1}}{n+1} + I \text{ (when } n \text{ is not equal to } -1)$$

Thus

$$\int \frac{dx}{x^2} = -\frac{1}{x} + I \text{ and } \int \frac{dx}{(a-x)^2} = \frac{1}{a-x} + I$$

where I is the constant of integration.

M21
$$\int dx/x = \ln x + I$$

It is this integral that gives rise to the frequent occurrence of natural logarithms in physical chemistry.

LIST OF SYMBOLS

A, B, C, D	Symbols representing chemical compounds
A	Frequency factor in Arrhenius equation
a, b, c, d	Initial concentrations of compounds A, B, C and D respectively
C	Centigrade (Celsius) temperature scale
C	conductivity
d	differential operator
exp	exponential function, e.g. $\exp x = e^x$
H	enthalpy
$\Delta H^{\ddagger}$	enthalpy of activation
h	Planck's constant
I	integration constant
K	Kelvin (absolute) temperature scale
K	equilibrium constant
k	rate constant
ln	logarithm to the base e (natural logarithm)
log	logarithm to the base ten
M	symbol for reference to Mathematical Appendix
M	molecular weight
N	Avogadro's number
n	number of molecules per cc
P	probability or steric factor
p	pressure
R	perfect gas constant
S	entropy
s	number of vibrational degrees of freedom
$\Delta S^{\ddagger}$	entropy of activation
T	absolute temperature
t	time
$t_{\frac{1}{2}}$	half-life
x	concentration of reactant consumed at time t

Z	number of collisions per cc per second
$Z°$	collision number
Δ	change in value of a physical quantity (final value minus initial value)
η	viscosity
θ	fraction of surface covered
ρ	density
σ	collision diameter
[A]	molar concentration of A

Note—the units of physical quantities are stated formally in this book. For example 'mole litre^{-1}' means 'moles per litre'.

INDEX